Living in

MORTAL TIME

*Conversation for Those
Who Have Never Died*

Living in
MORTAL TIME

Conversation for Those
Who Have Never Died

Richard P. McQuellon, Ph.D.

Michael A. Cowan, Ph.D.

WINSTON-SALEM, NORTH CAROLINA

Printed in the United States of America

ISBN: 978-0-9720747-0-4

DEDICATION

To the staff and volunteers
of the Cancer Patient Support Program
Comprehensive Cancer Center
Wake Forest University Baptist Medical Center
Winston-Salem, North Carolina

To our mothers: Kathleen McQuellon and Marie Cowan

To our wives: Cyndee and Kathleen

To our children: Meghan, Brendan, Kristin, Katrin,
Mairin, Kendall, and Rebecca

To our patients: They taught us how to
walk together with courage in mortal time.

Contents

Acknowledgments

The Cancer Patient Support Program (CPSP) at Wake Forest University Baptist Medical Center is a unique organization that includes six staff members, approximately 30 weekly volunteers, and over a hundred community volunteers who give of themselves tirelessly. Marian Douglas, Ann Hanes, Kathy Janeway, Skip Boyles, Carolyn Ferree, Susan Kennedy, and all the members of the CPSP Advisory Board have through the years given so that patients may benefit. We are thankful to our volunteers and especially to Ed Easley for his careful reading of an early draft of this text. Both he and Roger Jordan are on duty each week comforting patients and family members. They know, firsthand, what it means to enter mortal time.

We are honored to work alongside the nurses, physicians, physician assistants, chaplains, social workers and other health-care professionals who strive to reduce suffering and promote healing each and every day. We especially thank Hy Muss for his generosity and Bayard Powell, David Hurd, Julia Cruz, Frank Torti, Ed Shaw, and Ed Levine for their leadership efforts in our Comprehensive Cancer Center.

We are indebted to a number of our friends and colleagues who have read drafts of this text and offered useful reviews: Richard Chiles, Cyndee McQuellon, Dennis O'Hara, Kathy McShane, Tony Miller, K. Patrick Ober, Barry Maine, and Gail Hurt. All provided helpful and encouraging comments. Anne Adkins, a CPSP volunteer, gave us vision and help with the task of publishing. We thank Wilson Somerville for his editing prowess and the staff of Creative Communications at Wake Forest

University School of Medicine for design, layout and production of the final book.

Fr. Conall McHugh, OFM Conv., consistently provided encouragement with a simple question: "How's the book coming?" Canice Connors, OFM Conv., helped by asking, "Where are you called?" The community of Franciscan friars and Sisters of St. Joseph provide daily sustenance for the soul living and working in mortal time.

Finally, we thank the following for supporting this project: Ann and the late Herb Brenner; The Kathryn A. Millward Fund; The Barbara D. Smitherman Memorial Trust; The Bertha Long CPSP Fund; The Higgenbotham Memorial CPSP Fund, the Mary B. Driscoll Memorial Fund, and the Belk-Glenn Fund for Cancer Patients. Their foresight and generosity gave us the time and resources to write and produce this book.

RPM
MAC

ON EARTH[1]

Resurrection of the little apple tree outside

my window, leaf –

light of late

in the April

called her eyes, forget

forget –

but how

How does one go about dying?

Who on earth is going to teach me –

The world

is filled with people

who have never died

– Franz Wright

OPENING

When Mary's physician told her that her breast cancer had returned and spread to her lungs and liver, her reaction took him by surprise. The young physician in training felt that Mary didn't understand the seriousness of her predicament. When I spoke with Mary in consultation she was sitting at the bedside in some discomfort but managing her pain reasonably well. She understood that her cancer had now moved to her liver and lungs and that it was not curable. She said that her main physician was "the man upstairs," but she also believed, "God works through people like you and the doctors and nurses." She further stated that she trusted her doctors and relied on their input. However, she was in the hands of God who would be the ultimate physician in her case. She was dignified, humble, and unafraid of talking about what might lie ahead for her. She had buried her father and cared for a brother disabled by a stroke within the past year. She had grown familiar with the possibility of dying. Her caring physician was not critical of her, but puzzled by what seemed to be her "denial" of her situation. She was prepared to discuss the limits to her life, yet hopeful that God would touch her with a miracle. For her this was not denial but rather a deep faith in the future, whatever it held.

Mary was calm in the face of her diagnosis, her physician was puzzled by her response to life-threatening information, and the consultant was struck by their differing responses. This incident highlights the power of death's multiple meanings to shape feelings and behavior. While only one person in this story faces grave illness, all three—the patient, her physician, and the consultant—are facing death. Yet, death has a different meaning for each of them, as it does for everyone it touches. These meanings color how people feel, think, and communicate as they turn to face death together.

The Birth of Possibility

A profound, but rarely considered reality is that the moment of our birth heralds the possibility of our death. We enter mortality when we are born. Youth with its promise rarely considers this. Why should it? In this book we will consider a reality that cannot be evaded, the mortal time zone entered when a person is dealing with possibly fatal illness, and the prospect of ending becomes all too real. At one extreme, the ever present reality of our mortality can be trivialized by offhand comments like, "We all have to go sometime." At the other, it can provoke morbid preoccupation. In these pages, we will navigate between these extremes of obliviousness and obsession.

What you will read here is drawn from nearly 20 years of intense experience with patients and their caregivers in a comprehensive cancer center as well as personal encounters with serious illness and dying.[1] In the field of cancer treatment, the term "caregiver" is often used to describe family members who have a major part in assisting a relative diagnosed with some form of cancer. We broaden that meaning to include medical professionals, friends, and non-family members such as hospital and hospice volunteers, who are involved in the care of patients facing serious illness.

In Part I: "The Many Meanings of Mortal Time," we consider the personal experience of patients and caregivers confronting a life-threatening diagnosis, and focus on the role of meaning in that confrontation. This section lays the groundwork for addressing the main question of the book, which appears in Part II: " Hope from Conversation," namely, how can patients and caregivers walk together with compassion and honesty in the inevitably disturbing company of mortality? In Part III: "For Those Who Have Never Died," we focus attention on things to mind when companioning others in mortal time. Given the intense emotions that arise in the face of death, it is hard to think clearly and reflect wisely when its prospect looms closely. Finally, we close with a word to caregivers about the hazards and blessings of moving in mortal time. We have placed questions for reflection at the end of Parts I, II, III , and the closing. These are intended to help patients, professionals, volunteers, and family caregivers consider the issues that we raise. They may also encourage both personal reflection and compassionate, consoling conversation among family, friends, and colleagues and assist small groups in discussing these topics.

Living With Mortality

This is not a book about dying, but rather about living gracefully with the possibility of death, whether it is on the doorstep or in the unforeseeable future. We have written it for lay people and professionals, and with a particular concern for friends and family who are accompanying a loved one during the diagnosis and treatment of a life-threatening illness. We use the term "life-threatening" in these pages to refer to situations where the patient believes that their illness could end their life in the immediate or distant future, while recognizing that they may far outlive their predicted life span.

Michael Lerner has likened receiving a cancer diagnosis to being dropped into a jungle with no survival skills or tools.[2] Often without warning, the patient, family, and friends find themselves on alien, anxiety-provoking ground. Here we provide map and compass for those facing death directly or as companions of loved ones facing territory that is inherently frightening. We offer reflections on the momentous rite of passage that we call "mortal time" through real-life vignettes and possible answers to questions that real people have when dropped into mortal time. We consider how one best listens to and speaks with one facing life-threatening illness, because our major purpose in writing this book is to encourage frank, life-affirming discussion of the prospect of death for those facing it together. Death is not unspeakable and need not be avoided until the "last minute," when a precious life is ebbing quickly, and opportunities for dialogue may be dramatically limited. In fact, embracing death honestly and compassionately can open the hearts of family members, friends, and other caregivers to speak of life in all its richness and promise, to the end and beyond. Dying is part of living, and needs to be "talkable." In a culture famous for collective denial of death, this means going against the grain. We do not advocate morbid preoccupation with death, nor pushing the "death talk" on patients, but rather courageous acknowledgment and honest, sensitive engagement with a central fact of life: all of our lives are time-limited. Mortal time is only a reminder of that challenging, existential truth, which each of us faces, more or less consciously, throughout life. For the professional caregiver in cancer medicine, mortal time is a daily companion, but we all face opportunities to befriend mortality over the course of a lifetime.

The approach you will find in these pages emerged from direct experience with patients and caregivers contending with diagnosis and treatment of cancer, but we believe it is applicable for anyone facing life-threatening circumstances. We have changed the names of all patients whose stories we share, remaining true to their basic situation while protecting their anonymity. Our hope is that people facing mortality, those who love them, and those who care for them as professionals and volunteers will find in these pages compassion for their suffering, the consolation of meaning, and a measure of practical guidance for the challenging journey through mortal time. It awaits us all.

PART I
THE MANY MEANINGS OF MORTAL TIME

"In a dark time, the eye begins to see,
I meet my shadow in the deepening shade." [1]
                              - Theodore Roethke

Mortal Time

By "mortal time" we mean the experience of human beings confronting the prospect of death.[2] This confrontation can stimulate intense feelings, a flurry of thoughts, and erratic or unusual behavior. In the broadest sense, mortal time is entered whenever death comes near, and that can happen either directly or vicariously. Momentarily losing control of a car on an icy street, signing a medical consent form where death is a possible "complication," or having an aircraft on which one is a passenger drop abruptly in the sky are direct experiences of mortal time. A loved one's cancer diagnosis, losing a family member in an automobile accident, or a child gone missing are vicarious experiences of mortal time.

As we noted in our opening, the focus in this book is on the particular and powerful instance of entering mortal time that occurs when someone receives a diagnosis of life-threatening illness. It may be one in which a progression toward death is imminent, or where there is only the possibility that someone may die from a disease over some period of time. There are, of course, many instances in which people far exceed their statistically predicted life span. Mortal time may stretch from days to years, with patients encountering both helpful treatments that lead to periods of remission and recurrences of disease requiring additional treatment. Some chronically ill patients may never experience a time when it is apparent that they are dying. The interval between living and dying that we are concerned with here is not primarily defined by days, weeks, and months. The hallmark of mortal time is the prospect of death confronting a person and those who care for him or her. When someone enters mortal time directly, their caregivers enter the same time zone vicariously. What they do there together affects the quality and meaning of life for all involved.

When Mary, whom you met earlier, was told by her physician about the return and spread of her cancer, both of them entered what we call mortal time, one directly, the other vicariously. The diagnosis of a likely terminal illness brings home, abruptly and intensely, the reality of death to those involved. When such an illness is diagnosed, all those it touches are thrown into mortal time, ready or not. This stark meeting with mortality boils down to two inevitably disturbing realities: someone is facing death, and those involved know it.

The Multiple Meanings of Mortal Time

If mortal time entails facing death directly or vicariously, what are the possible meanings of such a confrontation? Patients and caregivers encounter the imminent prospect of death as they do any other life-event, through the looking glass of their own personal history. Psychotherapist Jerome Frank called the unique perspective which each person brings to life situations the "assumptive world."[3] Think of your assumptive world as the story you have personally gleaned from living, discovering what life means and your role within it. That continually updated story guides you and all of us through day-to-day life, automatically for the most part. Each person's story makes possible and limits their interpretations of events. Those interpretations in turn make possible and limit how they feel and act in all of life's circumstances, including the inescapable one named death. For example, a first-born daughter of working parents with a mother on second shift would likely be thrust into a caregiver role early. She would regularly look after her younger siblings in the absence of parents. Her assumptive world or life story would likely have a very strong "taking care of others" component. These assumptions operate automatically, often as "shoulds," in this case as, "I should always be responsible for my brothers and sisters." This view would contrast with that of one who was the youngest of six, the "baby" of the family, always being taken care of by others as he was growing up. We all carry personal assumptive worlds, the product of our life experience and inherited capabilities. Assumptive worlds are both stable and changeable over time.

Shattered Assumptions

Mary held a strong belief that God cares and would continue to care for her. She had faith in God and the future even when cancer returned to shorten her life. This belief was the anchor of her assumptive world. She appeared unrealistic to her physician, not fully aware of her situation. His assumptive world did not include faith in God like hers. From his vantage point, she was in denial. From the consultant's perspective, Mary was not only able to comprehend the seriousness of her illness but empowered to face it by her conviction that she was in the hands of a higher power than medicine. People deal with the inevitable trauma of entering mortal time differently, depending on what they bring to it, according to their differing assumptive worlds. The personal assumptions of patients and caregivers shape the entire experience of mortal time.

Personal assumptions can be radically altered in an instant. As Ronnie Janoff-Bulman states, "shattered assumptions" can occur when any major crisis calls into question three universal, but usually implicit, assumptions that we all make: the world is benevolent, the world is meaningful, and we are worthy.[4] The diagnosis of a life-threatening illness can cast these assumptions into doubt and even "shatter them to pieces." This leads to heightened anxiety as we confront the illusion that we are immune to death. How we adjust after our assumptions are shaken depends on whether we despair or remain hopeful upon entering mortal time. How does hope survive shattered assumptions? How is meaning restored in a now time-limited world?

In order to appreciate how people create meaning out of life-changing experiences, it is useful to consider how meaning happens. One classic view is that the meaning of something resides within it. Another is that the meaning of something is in the mind of the interpreter. We take a third position: Meaning happens "in between," when an event and its interpreter meet. We don't feel, think, and act the way we do because something happens, but rather because of what it *means* to us. In mortal time, patients and caregivers meet death, and what that meeting will be like depends both on what it brings to us and what we bring to it. What we bring is our own assumptive world, which could include many experiences with life-threatening illness and death or none at all.

Coping in Mortal Time

David Cella has described four styles of coping with cancer that reflect different assumptive worlds: realists, opportunists, zealots, and fighters.[5] These styles may be thought of as tendencies to act in a certain way when faced with a threat to life.

Each represents one way that people respond to entry into mortal time, but they are by no means exhaustive or exclusive. Many people combine two or more of these coping styles. **Realists** assume that the odds are against them. Cella describes them as "pessimists who see little hope in the situation." (We rename this group **pessimists**, and save the term **realists** for those who can tolerate even the prospect of death without sinking into despair.) **Pessimists** have a tendency to stress the negative or unfavorable or to take the gloomiest possible view of a situation. They are likely to consider any optimistic statement as "false hope," rather than seeing a range of possibilities in their illness from treatment options to the possibility of death. **Opportunists** would like to reduce the daily stress that accompanies treatment and the awareness of one's fatal illness; however, they are not willing to expend the energy it takes to do so. They simply wait for those around them to provide the right opportunities for cure or help. Then they will take advantage of the situation. **Zealots** believe strongly that the mind has the power to heal the body. They may make professional caregivers uncomfortable because of their strong convictions and often unconventional beliefs. For example, they may enthusiastically embrace non-medical therapies such as herbal preparations, colon cleansing, Reiki, and healing touch to the exclusion of accepted approaches like chemotherapy. Their frenetic activity and intensity help relieve the natural anxiety that comes with suffering and the possibility of death. Some zealots would rather pursue one more unusual avenue than contemplate the prospect of their own death. **Fighters** are adaptive copers. Like zealots, they believe in the power of the mind to influence the body. However, unlike zealots, they are fully aware of their mortality and have the ability to take useful messages and information from the popular press, research or their professional caregivers, rather than investing hope in unorthodox cures. Fighters generally do well by adopting an adaptive, optimistic attitude as well as developing a factual understanding of the powerful biology of cancer. One patient told us that she didn't fit any of these labels neatly, but was a blend of realist and fighter, paying close attention to the facts of her disease but never giving up on treatment possibilities. As an alternative to the metaphor of "fighting" life-threatening illness, Carol Orsborn has suggested a fifth type of coper—*peacemakers*—those who follow the ways of letting go and relaxing deeply in response to critical illness, especially cancer.[6] Because they bring such different assumptions to life-threatening illness, realists, pessimists, opportunists, zealots, fighters and peacemakers experience mortal time quite differently as patients and caregivers. It would be true to say not just that each faces death differently, but that each faces a different death.

What to Expect in Mortal Time

While patients bring diverse assumptions, feelings and coping styles into mortal time, four common experiences await almost everyone who arrives there. ***First, entry into mortal time is profoundly disturbing.***

When Dustin began having trouble swallowing, he assumed it was a symptom that would pass. When it persisted and became worse he saw his general physician who sent him to a gastroenterologist. An endoscopy and biopsy revealed cancer of the esophagus. The diagnosis shocked and frightened him, catapulting him into mortal time abruptly and painfully. He called to discuss what was happening prior to talking with the doctor about a treatment plan. He was understandably distressed and on the verge of tears, during our conversation. "I'm sorry. These tears just seem to come in waves. I don't have much control. This has never happened before. I'm not at work today; I'm out shopping for a car with my son. That helps to keep my mind off it."

The language of others can force people into mortal time harshly. Statements such as, "About 15-20% of people with your stage of illness survive five years or more," delivered matter-of-factly, are shocking to someone unaccustomed to the statistical language of medicine. It can be especially painful if followed by, "If I were you I would get my affairs in order." Such comments may suggest gross insensitivity or tactlessness on the part of medical providers. While this may be the case, the reality is often more complex. Patients often elicit blunt statements by demanding that healthcare providers "be straight with me" or "give me some kind of time frame." One of our patients was highly distressed when her physician called her on the phone and said, "You have colon cancer and need surgery immediately." She described him as curt, short, and "uncaring." It was his manner which disturbed her the most. The physician making this phone call may have been simply attempting to convey the gravity of her situation in order to encourage her to move quickly. We aren't blaming either party, but simply pointing out the complexity of communication in such intense situations, and how easily it can go wrong.

It is senseless to find fault with caregivers or patients who may fail to communicate well in these trying conversations. Both are attempting to converse about a nearly incomprehensible event, that is, the prospect of death for a human being. Professional caregivers and patients, however, do not enter these exchanges as equals. The former are not superhuman, but are rightfully expected to assume greater responsibility for how the conversation proceeds because of their training and experience. Fortunately, medical educators are ever more aware of the necessity of giving their students some training in respectful, compassionate communication.

A second common experience in mortal time is preoccupation with the prospect of death. The statement "People with your disease usually have 6 to 12 months to live" is stark and terrifying. It can set off a cascade of worries and near constant rumination about the illness, financial concerns, tearful episodes about the anticipated future, and intense anxiety about what might happen to children. Fortunately, people cannot think about imminent death constantly over a long period of time. To keep the prospect of death in the forefront of one's mind continuously robs the present of hopeful, life-affirming activity. This results in a form of "the feared future dominating the lived present." A total focus on dying is impossible because the mundane tasks of living—working, eating, dressing, sleeping, and so on—will invariably interrupt even the most intense preoccupations. The focus of patients and caregivers on endings will shift from foreground to background, over a period of moments, hours, days, weeks, months, even years. This fluctuation depends upon many things including the frequency of ongoing medical tests, medical news regarding the success of treatment, the occurrence or recurrence of symptoms, the patient's own understanding of progress in the development of new healing treatments for their condition, and the responses of other people to their condition. The uniquely personal experience of mortal time is a constantly changing kaleidoscope of fears, fantasies, and worries, including the waxing and waning of hope for the future.

A third common experience when people encounter mortal time is a shocking sense of loss. Life's formerly taken-for-granted possibilities are shaken by the prospect of death. These losses include every aspect of life—family, friends, career, interests, and commitments—including, at the deepest level, the loss of self, the end of "me." In one disruptive instant, the hopes and dreams on my horizon become impossible. The unspoken assumption that "life will go on" has been snatched away in one terrible moment, and transformed into "life will go on without me." An inevitable but unexpected ending has suddenly come into sight, transforming everything that stretches between now and it. People feel and express this sense of loss at the prospect of death in widely varying forms, depending, once again, on the assumptions they bring to it. One may expect to find nothing beyond this life or as one patient said, "When I am gone, that is it, nothingness, blackness, the end." Another may see death as the transformation of herself into a transcendent being with eternal life in the hereafter.

Finally, no one returns unchanged from a confrontation with death. The changes may be dramatic, taking surprising, even liberating, twists.

"My cancer was a gift to me." When Joyce said this her consultant was puzzled. She went on to say that once she had gotten over the initial treatment

15

and reconsidered the nature of her life she knew that some things had to change. She saw that she was living in a rut. Her life consisted of working eight hours a day and coming home to cooking, cleaning, and managing all the household chores. With new resolve and energy, she told her husband that things were going to be different. Her life had been changed forever by the possibility of it shortening. Even though treatment was proceeding well, and she had an excellent prognosis, her brush with the possibility of death had changed her forever. "I'm just not going to do that anymore. I'm not going to work full time and do everything at home. The chores are going to be shared or else. This is a whole new life for me."

These words come from a woman who had not spoken up in her marriage for many years. They convey the sense of urgency to deal with things differently that mortal time brings to some. Precious life is waning and it's time for changes. Joyce found new and liberating possibilities awaiting her in mortal time. One of the consequences, of course, is that loved ones and others will have to change, also, as relationships find a new balance. A life-threatening diagnosis for one person means changes for everyone in that person's web of relationships. Joyce's cancer diagnosis caused her to examine her most important relationship, her marriage. Unexpectedly, hope for a better life arose from seeing her marriage through the lens of life-threatening illness, giving her a different perspective. Mortal time has its own graces.

How we experience oncoming death depends largely on what we bring to it. How mortal time feels and what we can do within it, depends on what it means to us.

The Challenge and the Invitation of Mortal Time

Human beings live with three fundamental questions, the same ones that give rise to the great fruits of culture—religion, philosophy, literature, music and art:

- Where did I come from?
- What is my purpose?
- What is my destiny?

Such profound questions rarely emerge in daily life. Weeks, months, years, even a lifetime can slip away without a serious brush with them. But particular life events—birth, a close call in traffic, serious illness, or unexpected blessings—have a way of bringing them up, inviting at least a moment of reflection in passing. Ever since human beings emerged within the cosmos some 200,000 years ago, one life event above all others—our impending death or that of a loved one—has been the prime provoker of meaning-of-life questions. The questions of origin, purpose and destiny invite deep reflection with no guarantees. People find different answers; some are liberated, some burdened down. The question of purpose—what am I doing for what reason—is an especially powerful motivator since its answer can bring meaning. We focus primarily on the issue of purpose and meaning in the next section.

A Question of Balance

Anna Ornstein, a survivor of Auschwitz, has written eloquently of how we human beings always live in the balance of hope and despair.[7] The source of hope is meaning; the source of despair is meaninglessness. Most of us continue on our way from day to day because we find enough value and significance in our daily work, family, and civic life to keep us going. When meaning sags a little, we find ourselves asking, "Is this all there is?" Depression intensifies such questions, and can undermine meaning radically, throwing us into the abyss of despair. Past a certain point, despair can move human beings to its logical consequence—suicide. Absent hope, life is literally unsustainable.

The everyday hope and purpose that keeps us going is interrupted by impending death. Those who find themselves in mortal time, and the ones who care for them, are vulnerable to despair. For some, the balance of hope and despair is precarious. Professional caregivers often err on the side of not encouraging "false hope" for patients. The ethical obligation of professional caregivers is to present to patients diagnosed with life-threatening conditions a picture of their situation based on accurate medical knowledge. This casts patients and professionals into very challenging conversations. What is a physician to say to a patient who asks, "How long do I have to live? I want to see my grandchildren grow up." Would it be giving false hope to say, "Let's do the best we can" to a man with advanced cancer with an expected life span of 6 to 12 months? We discuss the idea of "false hope" in more depth in Part II.

The Prospect of Despair

In mortal time, we feel the anxiety and vulnerability of the balance between extended life and impending death acutely, and may well find ourselves tipping toward despair momentarily or for extended periods. What is it that threatens the meaning of life itself? One great student of the human condition offers this answer: too much complexity, too much evil, or too much pain.[8] "Too much" simply means more than we can bear. In mortal time, our own pain or that of those we love can become more than we feel we can bear. The emotional signal that we are approaching the limit of bear-ability is the tug of despair, calling into question our ordinary lives and agendas, raising the fundamental questions of meaning, draining away our resolve and energy. Here, in mortal time, those questions face us not as academic exercises or voluntary personal growth activities, but in all their high voltage, anxious, existential, spiritual power.

"I am a dead man." These shocking words initiated a bedside meeting with Thomas, a 19-year old college student who had recently completed chemotherapy for acute leukemia. The treatment had failed and he was now being prepared to undergo bone marrow transplantation. He understood the poor odds of this procedure for him and was in despair about the chance of cure. His powerful words stunned the consultant, even after 15 years of encounters with cancer patients. What does one say to a young man who makes what might be fairly characterized as a realistic and truthful statement? It was difficult to respond beyond an initial nod in recognition of his plight. After all, platitudes aside, what is one to say in the face of authentic despair? What motivates a person to describe himself as "a dead man" in the presence of others? And how does a caregiver respond to such intense communication?

"I am a dead man." These are the words of a person acutely experiencing what we call mortal time, a person who realizes that death is near, in this case, even in the inner sanctum of high tech medicine. This self-pronounced death sentence reveals a young man's agony on the terrain of despair, and issues a stark, angry challenge to any caregiver daring to engage him on that terrible ground. They are words of revelation and invitation, of disclosure and challenge. They give us a precious, painful glimpse of how harrowing the entry to mortal time can be for patient and caregiver alike.

Meaning in Mortal time

However, mortal time is not merely a frightening event that we must cope with periodically, but also one with the power to enhance life by flooding it with meaning. The diagnosis of life-threatening illness can bear the gift of intense and precious opportunities to reaffirm cherished meanings and discover new ones. How so? Martin Heidegger offered twentieth-century philosophy's most influential account of the character and significance of death.[9] His penetrating insight was that death is not primarily a biological event facing us at some as yet undetermined future point; rather it is both a personal confrontation with the time limits of our existence, and the most powerful and challenging invitation to live the time we have as fully and truly as possible. Heidegger realized that the limit named "death" sets the boundary of our very existence. The fundamental psychological and spiritual demand facing mortal human beings is accepting that our lives are limited. Embracing the fact that we will die can propel us into living authentically. Failing to confront the fact of our finitude, that our lifetimes and possibilities are not endless, leaves us scattered, unfocused, and prey to the unending procession of cultural fads and addictions. Time "gets away" from us, and we realize too late that cherished hopes for ourselves, our families, and our communities will go unrealized. Facing the truth of Augustine's famous words: "When we finally lay down, we lay down for a long time," without succumbing to despair, demoralization, and paralysis, has a unique power to focus our attention and energize our living.[10] Acknowledging fully that our life story will end can propel us into writing it more fully and richly. Turning and facing the fact that we will die, so that we may live more fully, is the paradoxical promise of mortal time and perhaps its most profound source of hope.

Resolutely examining one's life in the face of death can lead to more meaningful and life-giving forms of thinking, feeling, and acting. Patients and caregivers in mortal time may be able to move past the moment of diagnosis in ways that allow life's vitality and dignity to be sustained and even enhanced in the shadow of encroaching death. This profound testing requires courage. James Yood, writing in the preface of Hollis Sigler's *Breast Cancer Journal*, has captured such courage well in his tribute to her: "This is the particular wonder of Hollis Sigler, to look squarely into the face of mortality and see it as an aperture between promise and despair."[11] Hollis Sigler was an artist and breast cancer patient. She faced her breast cancer diagnosis and treatment with the help of her art. Her paintings capture a kind of preoccupation with one's mortality that often proves the most serious threat to a life of quality in mortal time. Spending too much time contemplating cancer statistics can lead to obsession with death and dying. Patients with a diagnosis of cancer may be unable to live fully in the present because they are understandably preoccupied with the results of the next diagnostic test. The feared possible future of relentless disease dominates and diminishes

21

the present moment. A compassionate, receptive, and reflective posture toward dying buoys us up in the swells of despair, and stops impending death from wiping out life's meaning.

Velma, a 72-year-old woman who had been treated for acute leukemia had gone through her initial treatment and follow-up care over a period of two years. She had sustained one relapse and following the completion of her second round of chemotherapy was judged to be disease free. However, when the disease returned and she had a third round of chemotherapy, it failed. When her physician sat with her and explained that there were no more treatment options, Velma began to plan for the remaining days of her life. She was in the hospital and began to call relatives, friends, and loved ones to her bedside. While conscious, alert, and in no pain, she was able to talk openly with her entire family. She knew that she was going to die, and she embraced the opportunity for final conversation with those she loved. Her remarkable courage became a life-sustaining force not only for her family and friends, but also for the entire team on the medical unit where she stayed. She died peacefully, free of pain, in the company of loving caregivers.

But even genuine receptivity to death cannot substitute for the mundane coping that constitutes most of the day-to-day activity of those living in mortal time. In fact, ordinary activities often bring those who are dying up short, as their purpose is repeatedly called into question for one whose life may be ending. What is the point of taking out the trash when one is dying? Because it piles up, making living uncomfortable and unpleasant. The need to sweep the floor and pay the bills does not go away in mortal time.

Living in Mortal Time

Patients in mortal time may move back and forth from everyday coping to thoughts and feelings about their impending death. Reflective moments do not occur only in religious settings or while gazing out on a beautiful mountain vista. They occur regularly, surprisingly, and not always pleasantly. One of our patients had a recurrence of colon cancer; it had spread to her liver. She knew that it was not curable. One evening in a heated exchange she commented angrily and sarcastically to her husband, "Well, you won't have to worry about me for very much longer!" She was aware of intense feelings crashing through as she confronted her "death sentence" in mortal time. Yet she was not able to keep them from surfacing angrily with loved ones. Nor should she have. Anger is a most human response to loss, and needs to be heard and held by caregivers in mortal time.

Patients facing death often comment that distraction or change that takes them away from their ordinary routine helps them to avoid intrusive thoughts about their life-threatening illness. However, one can't remain distracted forever. In the words of a popular author, "Wherever you go, there you are."[12] We cannot escape ourselves; we take our thoughts and feelings with us wherever we go. While the most powerful distractions are often the simplest of activities—watching a child at play, taking part in a game of cards, reading a novel, or celebrating a family holiday—those who are dying and their caregivers cannot escape fleeting thoughts and anxieties amidst the everydayness of their lives. A painful paradox of mortal time, in fact, is that mundane events often call to mind and heart what will be lost for patients and caregivers alike to the death that is approaching. Living deeply in any situation means facing into what is really happening. This is as true for those of us living in ordinary time as for those living in mortal time. The latter, however, no longer have the luxury of denying the inevitability of death through the illusion of endless time.

Many patients and their caregivers shuttle back and forth, in and out, of acute mortal time over a lengthy period. The initial diagnoses of a life-threatening illness like cancer, followed by a failed treatment, or perhaps a series of failed treatments, are all painful reminders of the march of the disease. However, there are often long periods of remission where life without symptoms is restored. During these periods, people may leave behind the acute subjective experience of mortality and find the illusion of endless time temporarily, albeit partially, restored. Indeed, many types of cancer are like chronic illnesses, to be managed over long periods of time. Or patients' experiences of mortality become acute when all treatment options have been exhausted and the disease is free to run its course. Encountering a trauma such as the prospect of fatal illness inevitably shakes and tests what we have taken for granted. Thus, at a time when we most long for stability, all that we have taken for granted is assaulted by the prospect of death. Personal assumptions that have never been challenged are often shattered in mortal time.

Mary Jane had assumed that her bone marrow transplantation would eradicate her breast cancer for good. Her deep faith, strong web of supportive relationships, healthy life style, and "high tech" medicine were all powerful forces contributing to her cure. She was a fighter and badly shaken when the cancer returned. She faced a nagging question that challenged her fundamental belief: "Did I not have enough faith? Did I not believe strongly enough that God could heal me?" She had to recast her own story and assumptions about the power of faith to cure, wrestling now with Job's ancient question: Why me?

The experience of mortal time is profoundly personal. What death means to the dying and their caregivers, and, therefore, how they feel and act in facing it, depends upon the assumptions they bring, and how successfully they collaborate in facing what confronts them. Mary Jane's failed treatment shattered an unnamed, implicit assumption: "If I have enough faith, I will be healed."

Healing and Cure

Bob Stone had a very aggressive form of cancer that had spread. He spoke of his situation as follows: "I know I can't be cured of my disease. But I am healed emotionally and spiritually. This healing is every bit as powerful as cure; it's just on a different plane." [13] He drew hope from a spirituality in which physical cure is only one possibility. The Christian story, the center of his assumptive world, allowed him to interpret and feel death as a process of entering the next world. For many patients and caregivers the ultimate source of hope is faith. The hope of Mary, whom you met in our opening chapter, clearly resided in her Christian faith. Her belief and sense of what was happening to her were nearly inconceivable to a young physician in training who was treating her, because his source of hope was different—the rational, scientific paradigm where truth is determined by experimental research. Different life experiences create different assumptions and diverse sources of hope.

Nevertheless, There Is Meaning

What can anchor us, when we feel the tug of despair in mortal time? Early in his career, a student came to see the great teacher and philosopher Martin Buber. Failing to read between the lines, Buber did not realize until too late that the young man had come to him on the verge of despair, "not for a chat but for a decision." Upon learning of the subsequent death of his student, Buber asked himself what a human being expects when reaching out to another person in the attempt to ward off despair. His magnificent answer echoes down through the years: "Surely a presence by means of which we are told that, nevertheless, there is meaning."[14] When death's imminent approach erases normal, everyday hope, patients and caregivers alike need reassurance that meaning and hope endure. A most potent source of that reassurance is conversation, the subject of Part II.

PART I: THE MANY MEANINGS OF MORTAL TIME— QUESTIONS FOR REFLECTION AND CONVERSATION

The following questions are provided to help you reflect on the ideas presented in the text. They can be used to deepen your understanding of how these concepts apply to you. Or you can use them to stimulate discussion between you and another person or among members of a group.

1. Have you ever been diagnosed with a life-threatening illness or confronted death in some other way? If so, what was your immediate reaction? How did your loved ones respond?

2. Have you known a close relative or friend who has been diagnosed with a life-threatening illness? If so, how did this affect you and how did you manage?

3. What are some of your basic assumptions about life? About illness and dying? (For example, you may have the assumption that if you maintain a proper diet and exercise regularly you will be able to avoid disease.)

4. Mary's assumptions and faith in God differ considerably from those of the young physician who was treating her. What was the major difference between her assumptive world and that of her physician caregiver? How did this difference seem to affect their relationship?

5. Have you ever had personal assumptions "shattered" through the diagnosis of a life-threatening illness or other major life change?

6. When facing threats or crises, would you characterize your assumptive world as that of a realist, pessimist, opportunist, zealot, fighter, peacemaker, or some combination?

7. Diagnostic testing for possible medical illness can catapult one into mortal time. Have you ever had this experience? If so, how has it changed you? Were you preoccupied with the prospect of death and dying during this time?

8. The experience of mortal time often evokes the fundamental question of our origin, purpose, and destiny. How do you answer these questions personally?

    a.   Where did I come from?

    b.   What is my purpose? (Why am I here?)

    c.   What is my destiny?

9. It is common for those in mortal time to become preoccupied with the future when facing life-threatening illness. Have you had the experience of worrying so much about what would happen that it dominated your present living? If so, describe that situation.

10. The story of Velma illustrates a woman embracing the inevitability of her death. Do you know someone who has approached dying in this spirit? Do you think Velma gave up too soon? What do you think about her inviting family and friends to her bedside?

There can be no hope which does not constitute itself through a we and for a we.

I would be very tempted to say that all hope is at bottom choral.[1]

- Gabriel Marcel

Hope for the Day

Mortal time arrives when death's nearness has been announced in the form of a diagnosis. There is no turning back. Someone is facing the prospect of death, and those involved know it. Knowing that some patients defy the medical odds and recover, does not alter the likely outcome for everyone else, and may in fact result in a type of avoidance that helps no one. How individuals keep hope alive in the face of imminent mortality, as we noted in Part I, depends largely upon the personal assumptions they bring from past experience. The other major contributors to the meaning-making process in mortal time are caregivers. Professionals in medicine, mental health, and ministry, along with volunteers, family members, and friends, can help someone facing life-threatening illness gather meaning and value from a situation in which many find only despair. They do so by their willingness to be attentive, listen compassionately, and speak openly but tactfully with the one who is facing mortal time.

As we have already noted, the critical underlying challenge for patients and caregivers in mortal time is maintaining a sense of hope. The philosopher Gabriel Marcel captures the relational nature of hope by saying that it is constituted "through a *we* and for a *we*." America's legendary individualism too often obscures the truth that living—and dying—inevitably unfold in the company of others, for better and for worse. Nowhere is this awareness more important than mortal time. Maintaining or losing hope is not an individual feat or failure, but rather something that we do together, in relationships. The great Czechoslovakian writer and statesman Vaclav Havel said, "Hope is definitely not the same thing as optimism. It is not the conviction that something will turn out well, but the certainty that something makes sense, regardless of how it turns out. . . . Hope is a feeling that life and work have meaning."[2] Incurable disease can undermine or eradicate the hope that many of us operate on each day, that is, the natural hope of life extending into a distant future. Abrupt removal of that hope is devastating. For those who have entered mortal time, hope can mean the possibility of getting back to the old days, the way things used to be, getting back to normal. But entering a period of chronic, incurable illness eliminates that possibility for many people. Paradoxically, this can give those walking together in mortal time access to new and deeper wellsprings of hope.

Mary Ann was a long-time breast cancer survivor. She had learned what really matters through managing numerous recurrences and treatments over eight years. When asked how she managed her cheerful demeanor and daily motivation she said, "Of course there are many things that help me, including my friends, and my work. It helps a great deal to have something to look forward to, setting goals. I have little goals on most days and long-term goals also. Paddling down the Colorado River had always been a dream, but when I turned it into a goal it really helped me focus positively for a matter of months as we prepared for the trip. Having something to look forward to makes a big difference each and every day."

These words make it clear that hopeful goals pulled Mary Ann forward and helped her avoid being trapped mentally in an imagined, feared future by invasive thoughts about dying that could overwhelm each and every day. She figured out that the most significant threat to the quality of her present life was not the death on the way, but rather intrusive thoughts about what might happen in the future. Setting goals for living helped her avoid this common mortal-time dilemma.

Hanging Black Crepe

Gloom-and-doom partners are not the best companions in mortal time. One patient with a wry sense of humor has said, "I don't want them coming in hanging black crepe for me!" However, talking about incurable, life-threatening illness and death is serious business and elicits subtle variations of many different emotions, including fear, anxiety, and anger. It is usually best to begin conversations in mortal time by paying attention to the emotions of the patient and remaining alert and open to what she or he is feeling before sharing one's own feelings and thoughts. This receptive stance is an invitation to the other to say what's on their mind. Black crepe may not be the first topic in the conversation. Yet, when the prospect of mortality emerges, it need not obscure hope.

False Hope?

It is not uncommon in medical settings to hear warnings against giving patients "false hope." This is thought to occur when the medical team raises expectations about a cure when that is unlikely, or avoids talking directly about death. Professional caregivers share a wise wariness about giving false hope to patients and family members, lest they feel uninformed if the medical situation should go bad quickly. Unfortunately, this appropriate concern may result in overly dire predictions, or undue emphasis on worst-case scenarios. Would it be false to hope to be alive for a daughter's high school graduation in 12 months for a patient who has a projected life span of only 6 months? In such circumstances, how is a caregiver to respond to a question like, "Do you think I can make it to Susan's graduation?" Would "We'll give it our best shot" be giving false hope?

The late Stephen Jay Gould was diagnosed with mesothelioma in 1982 and told that his cancer had an eight-month median survival time. He crafted a pointed response to the predictors of doom entitled "The Median Isn't the Message."[3] Gould, who lived for 20 more years and died of an illness unrelated to mesothelioma, offers a salutary reminder of limitations and dangers of statistical predictions about the duration of life.

Conversation

The word *conversation* comes from two Latin roots, the prefix *con-*, meaning "with," and the verb *vertere*, meaning "to turn." When two or more people converse, they turn their attention to something together. Conversation creates bridges between professional and family caregivers and people in mortal time. Anatole Broyard has called the powerful moment of conversation where the professional caregiver and the patient experience a connection, the "click of contact." [4] This is the instant when eyes meet and understanding passes between two people in a powerful, compassionate, wordless exchange. In that "click," the patient becomes more than a bed number on rounds, an example of a diagnostic category, or a crisis to be managed; and the caregiver becomes more than an objective outsider. Now two human beings have connected, face to face and heart to heart. This can be indeed be an opening for a "healing conversation," or may remain an unspoken moment of deep human connection. Even a few such moments of deep mutual acknowledgment can make a very big difference to anxious patients. [5]

Healing Conversation

Conversation becomes both more important and more complex when one of the partners has entered mortal time. The personal assumptions and histories of patients and caregivers set in motion a rhythm of conversation between them that has the power to generate consolation and hope for both. Or they can produce polite civility, collusion in denying the severity of the patient's condition and the caregiver's real response to it, leaving the parties in minimal, uncomfortable contact. Or they can result in open conflict and alienation at this worst possible time. We offer the following practical guidelines based on our experience as conversation partners for those who wish to communicate well in mortal time.

Healing conversation has two requirements. The more deeply we accept both, the richer the communication that will result. The first is that we grasp our conversation partner's take on things; we "get" what's happening as he or she feels and sees it. **We listen carefully.** Understanding another means seeing a situation from his or her point of view. *Empathy* is one word for such understanding. To empathize is to grasp both the events and the feelings conveyed through another's disclosure, to make a disciplined effort to set aside our thoughts and feelings and walk in the other's shoes for a time. The events are the facts of the conversation, as delivered in words. Feelings signal emotional tone and intensity. Feelings are usually expressed by how words are spoken, including non-verbal signals, and are much more complex than any transcript of words can capture. Empathy, which we discuss in more depth later, requires both attentive listening and appropriate eye contact to fathom the emotional content of a patient's conversation. Caregivers who can turn toward the subject of death in an empathic manner with those who are facing it, invite the possibility of hope-creating conversations.

The second requirement of healing conversation is that we put into words our response to what is happening. We must say what we think, feel, believe, desire, question, and so forth in communicating with another. **We respond thoughtfully**. The letter to the Ephesians in the Christian scriptures puts this requirement in the simple, challenging form of "speaking the truth in love."[6] Note the double obligation here. "Speak the truth" means call things as we really see them; "in love" means with profound respect for our conversation partner. Anyone taking relationships seriously feels the tension inherent in honest, loving speech. Given the inherent anxiety of the mortal time zone, it may be equally important to "hold the truth in love" at certain times. Something may be true, but that doesn't mean that I can hear it from you right at this moment, no matter how tactfully you put it. For example, it may be true for some patients that "chemotherapy is very hard" or that "a particular type of cancer almost always comes back," but saying that to a person newly arrived in mortal time is likely to be misguided honesty, perhaps betraying a caregiver's discomfort more than a patient's need to know something. Speaking the truth in conversation is a process best informed by experience, compassion, and wisdom.

While the requirements of healing conversation are simple, namely, to listen and respond, the communication process itself is a complex matter of mutual interpretation. The capacity for language is wired into every human being. But accurate interpretation and skillful use of language is acquired over many years. As noted earlier, even skilled professionals with highly developed communication skills can feel awkward and out of place when encountering someone in mortal time.

Talking *in* mortal time is different than talking ***about*** mortal time. The subject matter of conversation in mortal time may be explicitly or implicitly about dying, or about other things entirely, depending upon patients' and caregivers' dispositions, abilities, openness, and needs at particular moments. The primary requirement is that both partners enter these conversations with respect and awareness for the gravity of the situation. Given that attitude, the dance of conversation can take on an endless variety of forms and address any and all relevant subjects. A person may wish to discuss the prospect of death openly and often or be able to make only fleeting references to it. When conversation partners in mortal time are able to tolerate the topic of death without fear that they are "giving up" on the patient by acknowledging the possibility of death, healing conversation occurs.

Talking About Mortal Time

When Natalie learned about her diagnosis of breast cancer she was also told that surgery was not recommended. The breast cancer had metastasized to her liver and it would not be useful to operate. She was told that she had a life span of approximately nine months. She underwent three horrendous rounds of chemotherapy that made her very sick. Subsequently, she discontinued her chemotherapy treatments. Surprisingly, her tumor seemed to stabilize. When she came to speak with me she said, "I was supposed to be dead by now. . . . the problem is despair." She went on to describe many life difficulties, the cancer diagnosis and dismal prognosis being just one of a litany of problems. She wrote eloquently about the importance of discussing this:

> *"I speak of space"—the "space where I face death, the space where we talk together. . . capturing the moment, counting the breath, attempting to be in the now. Facing death together. Being in that space."*

Not everyone approaches mortal time like Natalie, with a poet's keen eye for observing the soul *in extremis*. Doing so clearly provided her with comfort and relief. How is one to respond constructively to such profound self-revelation? Skill is important, but it is compassion expressed through empathy that makes *the* difference.

The training and vocation of the professional caregiver allows for openness to talking about death as one way of sustaining hope, but without forcing the issue. A possible conversation-opener initiated by a professional caregiver in this spirit is as follows: "Most people who are diagnosed with your illness have some worries about death and dying. We can talk about it whenever you want and leave it alone when you don't." Such a simple invitation is often met with relief since patients and caregivers alike can vacillate between being reluctant to speak of their fears and near obsession with them. These are hard, necessary healing conversations that require courage and hope. Few people approach talking about mortality with the fortitude of Natalie without a good conversation partner.

Conversation Partner

People coping with life-threatening illness need good healthcare and appropriate medications as part of the healing formula. Equally important is tending to the emotional and spiritual needs of vulnerable people in mortal time through supportive companionship. It is a rare patient or caregiver who is not greatly distressed by the diagnosis of a life-threatening illness. The words that are used in these life-changing diagnostic encounters can stay with people for a lifetime, for better or worse. We have all heard examples of healthcare practitioners being curt and insensitive. One patient told of her physician who tried to be encouraging on the day after her surgery by quoting from Shakespeare's *Julius Caesar*: "Cowards die many times before their deaths; the valiant never taste of death but once."[7] Her spirits were low; she was uncomfortable and not in the mood for pep talk from a surgeon quoting the words of a Roman general. Any caregiver will have bad days in mortal time, but fortunately most are skillful, caring professionals who do their best to provide accurate information in a compassionate, respectful manner.

Primary Conversation Partner

Family, friends, ministers, and health professionals are ordinarily the primary conversation partners of people in mortal time. Words cannot change the facts of the situation, but they can shape what they mean and allow for mutual expression of feelings. Knowledgeable professionals are in a position to give accurate information respectfully; family and friends are in a position to listen deeply to the hurt and fear of patients who may be experiencing what can become an overwhelming sense of loss. Healing occurs in mortal time when a caregiver takes in the experience of his or her suffering companion with compassion, sharing the burden of mortality. The simple saying "A burden shared is but half a trouble; a joy that's shared is a joy made double" applies here. Having a companion in mortal time, to "just talk" about everything, the light and the heavy, is a healing elixir. We say more about such companionship in Part III.

So, empathy and honesty are the basic requirements for conversation that sustains hope. Every one of us has the capacity for both, and all of us can deepen those capacities. Mortal time brings the challenge and opportunity to do just that. We turn now to these basic requirements, first to empathy, then to honesty.

Empathy

Empathy is the specific behavior that allows one to enter the world of another. The experience of empathy has the power to shape who we become because it can put people in touch with their own voice, in touch with themselves. [8] It is the skill that puts feelings of compassion into action. It has two steps. First, as noted earlier, we must accurately grasp **what** the other person is going through and **how** they are feeling about it. Then, we must convey our understanding to them in some way, let them know that we "get it." Sometimes this can be done by a simple reflection back to the other of what we have heard in the simplest language possible. Sometimes words are unnecessary and a compassionate nod of the head or touch of the hand is sufficient.

Empathy can be powerful medicine for several reasons. First, the person fortunate enough to have good listeners for caregivers can hear themselves talk about their situation and perhaps gain new insight. They can clarify their own assumptions and interpretations of the situation, always a valuable outcome. This insight can lead to problem-solving action. This could be as complicated as coming to some resolution about the existential question "Why me?" or as practical as deciding on a scarf rather than a wig for a head covering. Putting our experience into words can open up new understanding and possible actions for people walking together in mortal time. This is not simple because the natural tendency may be to relieve the suffering of another by responding quickly, by shutting off feelings of sadness or distress. The person who says "I am scared" may immediately get a response that directs the conversation away from these feelings like, "Be strong, you can get through this." Such a response, while not inappropriate with proper timing, can short circuit the empathic connection before it is set. Second, naming the source of anxiety and fear often encountered in mortal time can relieve suffering. As we noted earlier, entry into mortal time can be abrupt and frightening. Naming fear is the first step toward mastery of it. With mastery can come relief, at least temporarily. Being in the company of a listener who is extending empathy is strong medicine. Yet, it is not easy to find empathy in oneself let alone others, as a volunteer wisely noted on her way to becoming "properly empathetic."

Becoming Properly Empathetic

During her long journey as a volunteer caregiver and courageous cancer survivor, Nina Ann Stokes, put it this way, "I was never really properly empathetic until I experienced the side-effects of chemotherapy." [9] These words by a wise woman illustrate a common human dilemma. We cannot directly experience the life of another, but can only do so indirectly through the quality of our empathy. Even after eight years of treatment for breast cancer that had recurred several times, as well as very active volunteer work with many patients, Nina Ann was learning what it was like to have numbness in her hands and feet, a hallmark side effect of some chemotherapy drugs. She was deepening her already considerable empathy by self-reflection and self-examination.

Listening carefully and respectfully allows one person to understand the experience of the other. The limits of our empathy are determined in part by our ability to allow differences to register. The caregiving companion with no experience of incurable illness may be lost when encountering a friend whose father has just died. How is one to empathize with an unknown experience? Can we truly understand someone when we haven't been through what they are facing? Nancy, a volunteer in our cancer patient support program and a "veteran" patient of two different cancers has a different perspective than Nina Ann. She says that without going through a cancer diagnosis, it is impossible to really understand what it is like. She emphatically says, "You just cannot understand unless you have been there." We respectfully disagree. No one fully comprehends what another is going through, not even survivors who have been diagnosed with the same life-threatening illness, although they may have insights that non-patients cannot grasp. Listening deeply to a patient or loved one and responding with empathy brings us as close as we can get to forms of suffering that we have not experienced directly ourselves.

Experience with an illness and treatment-related side effects may help in deepening empathic capacity. However, even if two people have the same diagnosis and treatment, both will go through a unique situation because of differences in their personal assumptions. The meaning of a cancer diagnosis will be interpreted by each person uniquely, and those meanings differ. An example of empathic connecting gone wrong is the patient who has had a bad experience with chemotherapy and assumes that it will be that way for everyone. Some people manage chemotherapy with virtually no side effects and miss no work, while others are nearly incapacitated by a similar course of treatment. This probably has to do with differing metabolic rates and other biological responses to chemotherapy drugs that vary among individuals, as well as personal history and the quality of available supportive relationships.

Receiving Empathy

Expressions of empathy are not automatically received as intended. One of us once accompanied a wise, caring physician as he met with a couple to discuss treatment planning. The chemotherapy approach so far had not been working and the patient's disease was progressing; it was a turning point in treatment, where neither cure nor containment was possible. The very aggressive cancer was advancing in spite of all best efforts. In gentle and clear fashion, the physician laid out his plan: there would be no more chemotherapy recommended as it would only make the patient sick and would not stop the disease. The patient sat stunned, with his wife sitting next to him and crying quietly as she began to grasp the gravity of the information. Cure was not possible. We sat for some moments with this couple while the oncologist continued explaining his reasoning for the recommendation. A later check revealed the patient had been discharged early. Within the next week, at the patient's follow-up radiation therapy appointment, this surprising exchange took place: "That was a very difficult conversation we had in the hospital. How are you doing with all that?" The patient's answer was astonishing: "He told me and just left." The patient's experience of this exchange was that the physician gave him information and then abruptly left. In reality the physician had spent a significant amount of time with the patient even though it was a very busy day of rounds in the hospital. But in such situations, the "facts" of the matter do not matter. What one of us had observed contradicted what the patient experienced. He felt abandoned. This underscores the complexity of these interchanges and the challenge to caregivers to listen carefully and communicate what they hear tactfully to the patient. Even when one does listen carefully and respond compassionately, the patient may not receive it that way. In all human relationships, and especially those unfolding in mortal time, it is good to remember a wise man's ideas about the human condition: "A situation which is perceived as real will be real in its effects."[10] This underscores the importance of a second basic requirement for conversation in mortal time after empathy: honesty.

Honesty: What Can I Say?

"I don't know what to say. I don't know what I should say. And, he doesn't know what to say to me." These poignant words came from David, a father unable to speak to his son in the face of the boy's incurable illness. They illustrate one very important question for anyone accompanying someone through the diagnosis and treatment of a life-threatening illness: What should I say? Most people have little practice at this and even experienced professionals are often at a loss for words. Arriving in mortal time often renders words hollow. Consequently, we feel inadequate, don't know what to say, or when to say it, and may avoid the topic of what's happening to our friend or loved one altogether because we simply can't find words.

As we noted above, the second requirement of conversation is responding thoughtfully and truthfully. Many family caregivers get stuck on "the right thing to say." They worry that they won't have the right words and often look to experts to supply them. While it is true that people who have companioned others in mortal time extensively may have suggestions, every person with the ability to empathize can find their own words to meet the situation. Sometimes there is no need for words: a caring silence is all that is required. For the professional medical caregiver, the "truth telling" scenario is complicated even more by the ambiguity of medical information and the reality that fact and truth may not be exactly the same. Specifically, while the facts of the situation indicate a limited life span due to advanced disease, the truth of the matter for an individual may evolve altogether differently. In these circumstances honesty means understanding and communicating at the proper time both the best and the worst that can happen.

The Right Words

Words can take strange twists in mortal time, and not only for caregivers. A patient spoke poignantly about the challenge of communicating about a fatal diagnosis with loved ones:

> *"I knew she didn't know that there really was no cure, no magic bullet, unless the man upstairs decides to send a miracle. But I didn't know how to tell her. She only understood today when we talked to the doctor again. . . . But my son doesn't know. He is busy with his school, which has been very good to him, letting him postpone a test when I was so sick. I think I should tell him. I know this will be hard for him, I do not want to hurt him. . . . I need to tell my son about this, it needs to come from me."*

These are the words of a loving husband and father trying to protect his wife and son from the pain and suffering caused by the prospect of his dying. In this situation he is trying to find the right words to speak the truth to his wife and son about his harsh and sudden entry into mortal time and impending death at age 58. He wants a real conversation with his loved ones, and knows that it will be painful on all sides. He wants to make emotional contact by talking about his situation in mortal time, and yet as a good father and husband wants to protect his loved ones. He knew that his honesty would lead to suffering, yet, his courage moved him toward acknowledgment of a rapid entry into mortal time.

Conversation in Mortal Time

Anxiety and uncertainty are conversation blockers, and never more so than in mortal time. If we assume that a person coping with a life-threatening diagnosis is fearful and does not want to talk about their illness, we could avoid the topic or dive in anyway. The former could result in uncomfortable efforts to ignore the proverbial elephant in the living room; the latter can give rise to heavy-handed blunders like, "How do you feel about dying?" This question was asked by a co-worker of a patient newly diagnosed with early-stage prostate cancer, hardly a candidate for dying. In a misguided effort to say something, the coworker stuck his foot deeply into his mouth. Fortunately, the patient was not hurt but rather dumfounded by the insensitivity. In fact, it is rare for all but the closest relatives and healthcare team members to be in conversation with a patient who is literally on his or her "death bed." Most caregivers meet people who are living in a less acute experience of mortal time, where death is not imminent. It is difficult if not impossible to predict the hour, day, week, month, or even year of one's death in all but the most grave of circumstances. [11]

Caregivers may see deep sadness and anxiety in patients or loved ones and reflexively want to soothe them. Paradoxically, some attempts to comfort may compound suffering by distancing companions in mortal time from the issues at hand. For example, a common tendency of well-meaning family members is to say, "Let's not talk that way; don't give up now" in response to a patient's comment such as, "This cancer is going to get me in the end." Family caregivers may be extremely anxious, sad, or depressed themselves and not able to tolerate conversation that directly acknowledges the prospect of loss. Such situations often call for a particular kind of communication at a time when the conversation partner feels inadequate and even paralyzed. Both empathy and information may need to be communicated, empathy for what the person is feeling and information to correct misconceptions. Cancer may well *not* "get you" in the end. Nevertheless, at this point in the conversation it is important to acknowledge the fear by responding with empathy first and encouragement later as appropriate.

Everyday Conversation with Friends

One sensitive survivor of initial diagnosis as well as recurrent episodes of cancer speaks of how important conversation with an extended circle of friends can be. He suggests that people continue to behave as normally as possible, include the survivor in gatherings, and continue "slap-on-the-back" greetings. It is of course important to be mindful of the patient's health situation but equally important not to dwell on it. This is a delicate, shifting series of judgment calls differing from one person to another, and from moment to moment with the same person. Some people welcome the opportunity for head-on, frank talk about their condition, while others dismiss inquiries with simple responses like, "I'm hangin' in there." Momentous as it is, the diagnosis and treatment of a life-threatening illness is only one subplot in a very large life. Other topics of conversation are important as well. Knowing what is timely for mortal-time conversations requires a kind of disciplined spontaneity. Mistakes will be made, and there is no shame in that.

Sometimes people search for empathy and are met with information or platitudes from well-meaning others or are simply ignored entirely. All too often we may be oblivious to the suffering around us, or unprepared to respond to it. In the short story "Misery—To Whom shall I Tell my Grief?" Anton Chekhov illustrates this last sad reality of being ignored.[12] In the story, Iona, a carriage driver, repeatedly tries to tell the story of his son's death to several of his passengers, who either ignore him completely or chastise him. In an ironic twist as the story concludes, Iona is feeding his faithful horse at the end of the long cold night. She is attentive and hears the story of Iona's son's death. "The little mare munches, listens, and breathes on her master's hands. Iona is carried away and tells her all about it." His horse extends listening to her master in a way that none of Iona's human companions that night could. The type of blatant ignoring of suffering illustrated by Chekhov would seem to be much worse than the mundaneness of a trite platitude offered by a listener.

Platitudes

A platitude is a trite or banal remark or statement. The natural tendency for many people, especially healthcare professionals, trying to be helpful to patients in difficult circumstances, is to respond with such platitudes as "Hang in there" or "Just take one day at a time." A specific platitude may become habitual for healthcare professionals or those who regularly come in contact with the frightened or bereaved. A once-in-a-lifetime event for the patient or family caregiver may be a daily experience for the professional using routine phrases to comfort, and certain platitudes may take on a ritualized quality, for better or worse. A ritual may be defined as any act or practice regularly repeated in a set precise manner for relief of anxiety. For example, "Let's hope for the best and prepare for the worst" can become ritualized in the daily practice of cancer physicians, who commonly see patients with very difficult medical circumstances. It could be repeated many times in one day by the medical practitioner, and yet its mention to the patient or family might be the first time they had heard it. The words may be comforting for both the caregiver and the patient or family member. The statement is usually very well received by most patients. Sometimes those with a spiritual sensibility add "and pray for a miracle."

A caregiver who lovingly accompanied his wife through an extremely difficult and painful breast cancer treatment said, "A bad platitude is better than running away." His own faithful companionship with his spouse in mortal time allowed him to state convincingly a basic ground rule for all who dwell in mortal time: show up and be present; make the effort to reach out, even when uncomfortable. Being there is the key. Platitudes may sound hollow and shallow, or inspirational and uplifting, to those receiving them and depending on the manner in which they are offered and the assumptions of those receiving them. Some common phrases used to comfort are:

> *There are no cancers that someone hasn't beaten.*
> *Cancer is no match for you.*
> *Tomorrow will be a better day.*
> *Miracles do happen.*
> *You can get through anything.*
> *This too shall pass.*
> *God has a plan for you.*
> *God does not give you more than you can take.*
> *Prepare for the worst, hope for the best, pray for a miracle.*
> *Things happen for a reason.*
> *Live one day at a time.*
> *This is a marathon, not a sprint.*
> *Time will tell.*

This is a small sample of the platitudes that those in mortal time regularly hear. They may be comforting and even useful to the person who simply does not know what to say. All too often, however, the effect of using platitudes to avoid the awkwardness of being with someone who is anxious and suffering is to put distance between the conversation partners. While a patient may come to the conclusion that such platitudes as "Things happen for a reason" can be comforting, this is not likely to be their immediate response. One patient told us that she was deeply offended and angered when, during the diagnostic interview, her oncologist offered that, "Your cancer is a gift to you, it will help you set priorities, and it will change your life." Again, while this may be true, and this patient actually decided after much reflection that it was, saying it during the early diagnostic period was an insult to her. "How dare you tell me that a diagnosis of cancer is a gift in the midst of anxiety and worry," she told her oncologist. Only patients themselves can conclude that cancer is a gift; that perspective cannot be shoehorned in on them. Just as drug dosages require adjustments based on patient characteristics like weight, so too, the type of conversation cannot be limited to a formula where all patients get the same word. The timing and "dosing" of language in mortal time is an art.

Other platitudes are sobering and jarring; they can frighten and do harm, depending on who says them, how they are said, and when and where they are spoken. Some examples are:

If you have to have a cancer, this is a good one to have.
If I were you, I would be taking all of my vacation time.
You can't take it with you.
You could get hit by a bus at any time.

I have been working here a long time and have learned
how quickly things can change.
Let me put it this way: you had better get your affairs
in order.
There is no hurry to have surgery; that cancer has
probably been developing in your breast for years.
Hard times build character.

Platitudes can be used for better or worse. On the one hand they can comfort; on the other hand they can do harm. The sensitive, experienced caregiver companion knows when to draw upon a useful platitude and when to remain silent, yet deeply present.

How Much Time Do I Have?

One of the more difficult conversations involves the person for whom cure is no longer possible. "How much time do I have, doctor?" is a question that most people consider with a diagnosis of any life-threatening illness. [13] Some ask it directly. This is no time for hollow platitudes, and it is important for professional caregivers to have some general philosophy on how to answer this question. One of our physician colleagues replies this way: "Ultimately only God can answer that question; I can't be absolutely sure as a doctor. But given your type of cancer, and your current status, if you were to ask me how long, I would answer a matter of weeks or months." One physician suggests that the following one-liner of a senior physician is very effective in this setting: "We will see where we are and we'll go from there." This masterful use of words leaves open possibility; the source of its comfort may be in its ambiguity. Possibility remains in these words, "We will see where we are." Of course some patients may need more specificity, which is where the art of medicine is so very crucial. Words have the power to comfort and energize or frighten and demoralize. It is very important that the healthcare team recognize this and use both kindness and skill in their day-to-day encounters.

People facing incurable illness may need and want a different type of conversation than the usual everyday chatter, since conversation can lose its meaning in mortal time without some acknowledgment of the gravity of the situation. However, all human beings also need the lightness of humor and the peacefulness of quiet contemplation without fear. Conversation can be both "heavy" and "light" when death is on the near horizon. All human beings walk the fine line between heaviness and lightness; between everyday banter and serious discussion; patients and caregivers in mortal time do so in a particularly demanding way. In our experience, most people who lose their existential balance in mortal time fall on the side of lightness, that is, not fully appreciating the gravity of each and every heartbeat, that each day may be one's last. Yet, there is no room for harsh judgment for what is the best way in mortal time. There are times when the immediate reality of a situation is better avoided. As the Peanuts character Lucy once proclaimed in articulating the philosophy of Runism: "No problem is too big that it can't be run from."

Healthy Denial

It is not uncommon in cancer care to hear, "The patient is in denial." This judgment misses the point that each of us attends selectively to the environment around us. Denial is the psychological process whereby people protect themselves from threatening information by blocking it out of immediate awareness. It is a more intense form of the selective attention of everyday life. The denial of death is so normal in Western culture that it is often a serious obstacle to real conversation in mortal time. However, it behooves everyone to walk carefully on this territory, never attempting to cram the "reality of the situation" as interpreted by the health team down the throat of patients or caregivers. Professional and non-professional caregivers often get caught in the expectation that patients should acknowledge and discuss their impending death openly, that they should have "the talk" with their professional caregivers, that they should "really face" their situation.

Angela had developed pain and shortness of breath as her primary symptoms before entering the hospital for a complete diagnostic work-up. It was discovered that she had a rare form of sarcoma which had actually grown into the heart muscle, placing her in imminent danger. Furthermore, the prospects of the tumor being responsive to chemotherapy were poor. Her young physician felt that she was in denial, especially when she talked about the distant future with her daughter who was then in kindergarten. I was asked to speak with her about her denial. In talking with the patient and seeing her somber mood and tears, it was clear that she understood the gravity of the situation. She was petrified by the possibility of leaving her young daughter to fend for herself in the world. However, she was not prepared to discuss her life prospects immediately. She did not want to have "the talk" with the medical team at that point, in that place. Her private nature made her uncomfortable with the regular team rounds, which included up to seven different people standing around her bed early in the morning. However, in a one-to-one conversation it was clear that she understood the gravity of her situation and the likely outcome.

Professionals can undervalue the importance and usefulness of avoidance and denial. Some forms of reality, death being one, cannot be integrated quickly. Heartrending prospects like being a single parent unable to protect her child, helpless in the face of relentless disease, simply cannot be faced easily or quickly without devastating psychological side effects, including despair. Many family members facing the diagnosis of an illness that can't be cured are understandably at a loss for what to say or do. On the one hand they desperately cling to hope for a cure and want to be hopeful for the patient. On the other hand, they may instinctively feel a need to talk at deeper levels, to talk about things that matter, to take final chances to communicate with precious loved ones whose lives may be ending. The need to talk about dying and death may be trumped by the social taboo against talking plainly in the face of death as well as by fears of the patient and family members about what to say.

There are many ways to acknowledge death's arrival and many ways in which people protect themselves from the anxiety that accompanies awareness that life is threatened with ending. In the vignette about Angela, the medical consultant felt that she did not truly understand the nature of her situation and that a rational discussion of her impending death was important so that she could tend to last things. He was acting with consideration by calling in the consulting psychologist and had the tact not to push her into "getting your affairs in order" immediately. Yet he felt a responsibility to help her see that her cancer was not curable. Since it had already grown into her heart, it was immediately life-threatening in ways that most other cancers are not. The stakes were high here and made even more difficult by the fact that the patient was a single mother of a six-year-old daughter who would need to be cared for. Such considerations on the threshold of mortality are gut-wrenching for all involved.

Healthy Conversation About Dying

There are countless variations of the type of conversation that may emerge in mortal time. The following vignette illustrates a common one: acknowledging and appreciating a good life together as it ends.

Mary is the older of two children in a loving family. She faced her father's diagnosis and likely fatal prognosis with courage and hope. However, when the disease progressed and left this normally vibrant man bedridden, the inevitable movement of his cancer became painfully evident. Mary longed for a different type of conversation with her father. She wanted to talk with him about his situation and yet he didn't seem to want to talk about death. Perhaps he wanted to protect his daughter and family from what he knew was inevitable. With conviction and courage, Mary raised the issue, asking him to talk to her about their life together. This brave and loving step forward opened the door for deep and intimate conversation between a caring daughter and her loving father in the days before his death.

This vignette shows us what might be gained in an effort to talk about "final things." Such moments offer deep consolation to both parties and treasured, steadying memories for the ones who go on living. In this case Mary courageously and gently spoke with her father about her deep sadness that soon he would no longer be with her. This "death talk" was really a "life talk," a conversation about how much he meant to her and how much she would miss him in the future. Who would she call now about car problems? She had the opportunity, in the midst of tears and laughter, to tell him all that he had meant over the years, to tell him that he would be in her heart and soul forever. However, not all such attempts end with acceptance and peace. Some patients may never want to face the prospect of their own death directly in conversation. They may choose to talk about it in metaphors, speaking of "endings," "moving on," and the like, or not addressing it at all, holding on instead to a stubborn insistence on a miracle. It is the sensitive caregiver who knows how to proceed with such delicate matters, when to push forward and when to remain silent, when and how to speak the truth in love or hold his or her peace.

Practical Reality

End-of-life conversation sometimes happens because of practical considerations; for example, the medical team needs to know what patients' wishes are should they be incapacitated. [14] Would they want "everything done" or prefer not to be subjected to the many machines that can prolong life? Because intense emotions are involved here, sometimes what is clear to the medical team is not clear to the family, resulting in prolonged, futile treatment that can actually increase patient and family suffering at the end of life. The entire period between the initial shock of diagnosis to end-of-life conversations involves living in an acute state of mortal time wherein the awareness of one's finitude becomes more prominent. Walking with patients and loved ones on this terrain can be deeply gratifying and profoundly challenging. One of the demands facing professional caregivers is not to settle for a purely instrumentalist view of an end-of-life conversation, i.e., "Let's get this out of the way," like any ordinary medical procedure. The sensitive task of negotiating orders about resuscitation early in a hospitalization often falls to the least experienced medical providers, i.e., residents and fellows. This can make for very difficult conversations with distressed patients, uneasy caregivers, and anxious young professionals all struggling on unfamiliar and anxious ground. Such conversations bring all participants, patients, and caregivers alike, face to face with their own mortality. How these conversations in mortal time affect caregivers is our subject in Part III.

PART II: HOPE FROM CONVERSATION— QUESTIONS FOR REFLECTION AND CONVERSATION

The following questions are provided to help you reflect on the ideas presented in the text. They can be used to deepen your understanding of how these concepts apply to you. Or you can use them to stimulate discussion between you and another person or members of a group.

1. What is it that gives you hope each day? What is it that leaves you depleted and feeling less hopeful?

2. Have you ever experienced the "click of contact" as described by Anatole Broyard? What was it like? What makes this experience different from other conversations you've had? Why might the click of contact be important with conversation in mortal time?

3. Have you ever been part of a "healing conversation?" What was the primary topic of the conversation? What was it about that conversation that was healing? What was healing for you or for your conversation partner?

4. Have you ever been in a situation where you wanted to say just the right words and yet didn't know what to say? What did you say/do? After having time to think about this situation how might you respond now?

5. What is the difference between talking *in* mortal time and talking *about* mortal time?

6. Do you know someone who always seems to have the right words? What quality do they appear to have that helps them do this?

7. Perhaps it's a little too much to expect to always have the "right words." What do you think? What do you do when you can't seem to find the right words, no matter what?

8. Have you ever made a spontaneous "lame" comment only to regret this later? What was it about the comment that you regretted?

9. Is it possible to learn how to be "properly empathetic?" If so, how would you go about this?

10. Have you ever had to talk with a physician regarding "Do Not Resuscitate Orders"? What was it like for you? How did you feel about the conversation? Was the caregiver considerate and helpful?

PART III
FOR THOSE WHO HAVE NEVER DIED

To everything there is a season
and a time to every purpose
under heaven.[1]

Ecclesiastes 3:1

Companionship in Mortal Time

There are many different types of companions available to people cast into mortal time. First and foremost are family members—a spouse or other partner, parents, siblings, children, cousins, and others. Professional caregivers in hospitals and hospices include nurses, physicians, physician assistants, clergy/chaplains, recreation therapists, pharmacists, nutritionists, and physical and occupational therapists. These caregivers often become like family during the diagnosis and treatment of life-threatening illness. Professionals who regularly work with patients in mortal time are in a position to be "expert companions," that is, special guides who have been there before and know the territory.[2] Friends from work and community may take on important tasks and supportive roles in mortal time. The fundamental task for the people who would accompany a person in mortal time is joining them as companions.

The word *companion* is derived from the Latin *com,* meaning "together" plus *panis* meaning "bread." From this root meaning we see that the earliest meaning of *companion* is one who joins together with another to share bread. Sharing a meal is a perfect metaphor for companionship, and bringing a meal to people remains a simple but profound way of offering companionship in hard times. A companion is one who accompanies another, a comrade, a friend, a conversation partner. Joining with another as a companion is the most powerful antidote to the despair that can accompany profound loss. Perhaps the most basic way that human beings become companions is through conversation. Hope arises from and strengthens a "we."

Kind Companions

People throughout the healthcare system can offer companionship through small gestures of kindness and compassion. For example, the receptionist is often the first person to meet the patient when they enter a cancer treatment center. There are gifted receptionists who have a friendly greeting and smile for all who enter. This sets a tone of warm companionship in a treatment setting. Likewise, housekeeping staff and maintenance staff may have daily contact with hospitalized patients. With a cheerful, gentle demeanor they make a great deal of difference in the simple exchanges of the day. In fact, some comments from non-treatment staff can sound a lot like a psychologist's intervention.

Melissa was hospitalized for many days for treatment of acute leukemia. Growing weary and discouraged, she was physically and emotionally exhausted and had begun ruminating about how bad things were for her. She was stuck in a rut and knew it. One day a maintenance man told her, "When I get down, I try to think of all the things I am grateful for and it helps me feel better." She heard this wise advice and began her own form of

> *self-talk, literally changing her mind by adopting this simple technique of cultivating gratefulness.*

The many brief conversations that occur around tasks that patients must complete whether they are hospitalized, coming for outpatient treatment, or receiving care at home or in hospice, are all potential mini-moments of compassionate companionship.

> *Ray volunteers every Wednesday morning in an outpatient cancer center where he hosts a hospitality room replete with windows, relaxing music, snacks, and fellowship. He interacts with many patients and family members as they wait for treatment or test results. He listens attentively, remembers details of patient and family lives, and delivers snacks to patients in treatment areas to help with the nausea that can develop. A cancer survivor himself, he often says, "I get so much more than I give. It is my privilege to volunteer."*

Good companionship sometimes means being available on the patient's schedule, rather than the caregiver's. In discussing his wife's breast cancer, Dan commented that he was not taking on any new responsibilities or clients in the near future so that he would be available for his wife's anticipated medical appointments and procedures. Her symptoms, including nagging shortness of breath, had become particularly acute over the past three weeks. She had not been able to work or venture too far outside the house, prompting him to increase his availability while coping with a busy professional life in order to sustain their finances. He was adjusting as necessary in order to be a vigilant, faithful companion at the critical moment on this difficult journey where the presence of ever increasing symptoms seemed to foretell an acceleration within mortal time. A particularly difficult psychological task here is to remain present and attentive when the task switches from addressing the episodic acute symptoms of a curable illness to managing the chronic symptoms of an incurable illness. Dan was contending with uncertainty in a way that profoundly affected his every scheduled move. At the same time that he was working mightily to be there for his partner, the feared future was beginning to dawn on him: "I can't help it. . . . I wonder what it might be like to be a widower someday."

Companionship can be made more difficult by complex family circumstances. For example, in a blended family where an ex-spouse is dealing with a life-threatening illness and is geographically separated from children as well as his former spouse, many challenges arise. Communication between the patient and former spouse can be strained by the prospect of reopening old wounds. This can also be a time of profound healing and forgiveness, and important resolutions that can set free the spirits of patients and caregivers for new life after death.

The Costs and Risks of Companionship

Being with someone who has entered mortal time produces a dual challenge for caregivers. The first task is being compassionately present to the person managing their illness. This can be as basic as quiet physical presence in a hospital room while both wait for the news following tests, or a more active conversational presence where people talk about the day's events, the meaning of illness, or the patient's possible death. Compassionate presence puts one at risk of absorbing the suffering of the patient. A second task is managing the anxiety created when caregivers confront the fact that they too are living in mortal time. Repeated exposure to the prospect of one's own mortality is distressing. Social scientists have given this a name: "death anxiety." Such encounters often raise the ultimate questions we noted earlier: Where did I come from? What is my purpose? What is my destiny? Such questions are not easily answered and may disturb more than comfort. This is an inherent risk of working in mortal time.

The effects of encountering suffering in mortal time on relationships are cumulative. Faithful companionship in illness can take its toll in any relationship; it will certainly do so when someone is facing death. The caregiver can literally be worn out by the demands of compassion in the midst of deep suffering. Human beings can only absorb so much suffering and anxiety. "Compassion fatigue" is a condition where too much suffering becomes overwhelming. Knowing one's limits and how to step back and recharge emotional batteries is an important spiritual discipline for those moving in mortal time. Support and self-care are crucial for those who would be faithful companions in mortal time.

Personal Virtues for Mortal Time

It does not take a professional degree to be a helpful companion in mortal time. It does call for the exercise and often the development of specific qualities that most people have: presence, sensitivity, courage, acceptance, respect, compassion, a sense of humor, and awareness of our own limitations.[3] We use the term "virtue" for these personal qualities, because they are not techniques or gimmicks but rather qualities of character arising from life experience. We all bring virtues to mortal time and may, if we embrace its challenges, deepen old virtues and nurture new ones during these privileged moments.

Presence is the ability to be with another person physically and emotionally. Being present may sound simple, but it is particularly difficult when external distractions (a busy clinic, active children) or internal distractions (anxiety, thinking about what to say) intrude. Being present does not mean absorbing another's emotions or collapsing under the weight of another's pain. The "fusion delusion," where one person is so wrapped up in another's emotions that they lose track of their own, muddies the water and confuses people in mortal time. Being present without taking over another's pain or projecting one's own feelings onto another is a complicated, delicate dance. Sometimes presence with boundaries proves impossible for a family member, so close to their loved one that they can sense their every emotion. Presence also involves physically attending to another. By "attending," we simply mean paying close attention. Being physically and psychologically present can be profoundly healing in and of itself even without words. In conversation, this is often as simple as following the lead of the patient by putting one's own conversational agenda on the back burner. Being at the side of a loved one for doctors appointments or sitting quietly at the bedside in the hospital are powerful opportunities for presence. The essence of presence is being there for the other, putting their needs first. Strong presence to another is not easily achieved. Not many of us are accustomed to suspending our needs and paying attention to another in an intense way for long periods of time.

Sensitivity refers to the awareness of the emotional state and needs of others and oneself. This state requires "people reading" skills—the ability to look at a person and make some accurate judgment as to what they might be feeling given their body language, voice tone, pace of speech, and any other cues that they may give off. It is always risky to assume you know what someone's thinking and feeling, even though body language can provide clues. Some people seem to have a knack for reading and understanding what another might be feeling. It is important that the person who is attempting to understand and be sensitive to the other not assume that he or she "knows what the other person is thinking or feeling." Tentativeness is golden here. For example, "You seem sad today. Are you feeling down?" is a gentle challenge and invitation to recognize underlying feelings that may be more or less in one's awareness. Sensitivity also involves being aware of one's own feelings so as not to confuse them with the feelings of another. It is all too easy to assume mistakenly that we understand the perspective of another person, particularly for caregivers who have been on the turf of mortal time with many people over many years. No two people experience mortal time in quite the same way, and one of the challenges is to maintain sensitivity to the unique responses of each individual.

Courage is required to accompany another in mortal time. It is the mental and moral strength to persevere in the face of danger and difficulty. The diagnosis of grave illness presents people and their personal caregivers with an immediate threat to their way of life and often a difficult path ahead through treatment and follow up care. Courage is a quality that can be cultivated, especially through repeated exposure to mortal time. Companions will often accompany their loved ones through many doctor appointments and difficult test procedures that can shake their resolve. Particularly distressing are the moments when outcomes of lab tests or scans are not good. The news that a patient "failed chemotherapy" is always hard, and often made bearable only by the presence of a fellow traveler, a companion in mortal time. In order to be there and stay there, companions must be able to tolerate this and many other distressing situations, like waiting for long periods of time to see doctors, missing work, and foregoing travel and normal leisure pursuits. One's former "normal" schedule becomes a thing of the past.

Acceptance comes from the Latin *acceptare,* which means to receive. Accepting another's illness and the demanding path that it may put one on is no simple task. For starters, it requires time simply to absorb the reality of life-threatening circumstances. Acceptance may bring a profound sense of peace. We want to underscore that acceptance is not giving up, but rather letting go of the effort to control a situation fraught with ambiguity and uncertainties. The disposition of acceptance is classically expressed in this excerpt from the "Serenity Prayer" of Reinhold Niebuhr:

> *God grant me the serenity*
> *to accept the things I cannot change;*
> *the courage to change the things I can;*
> *and the wisdom to know the difference.*

In the wise words of the Twelve Step tradition, acceptance means "letting go and letting God," however one conceives of a higher power.

Respect signals our appreciation of the worth of another. For people of faith this means receiving each person as made in the image of God. It is communicated both by what we say and how we act toward a person. The opposite of respectful conversation is often seen in today's "talk" shows where commentators routinely attempt to prove their intellectual superiority by shouting or arguing down others. Respect in conversation requires thoughtful, patient listening, responding with care and sometimes with deference to the other's personal circumstances. Respectful communication is ordinarily characterized by give and take. For physicians and nurses this includes giving simple and clear explanations of complex medical facts to patients and family members unfamiliar with the language of medicine. Doing so respectfully requires awareness of where the patient is starting from, understanding the situation from the patient's perspective. The task is made more difficult by a fact that we noted earlier: a once-in-a-lifetime experience for the patient is an everyday event for the medical practitioner. The medical person may be hard pressed to be patient when answering the same question for the fifth time that day, albeit from a different person. Often the same question is repeated by a single patient because the answer already given is startling and not comprehensible, even when given in simple language. In such moments communicators must strive to remember that what a person is really absorbing is not information, but mortality. An exhausted, exasperated caregiver may end up talking in a patronizing manner. Even when unintended, it is not the right ingredient for respectful interaction.

Compassion for another involves understanding what someone is experiencing, especially their circumstances and suffering. This can be both powerful and painful, as anyone who has held a sobbing loved one on their lap knows. Compassion is the value that drives empathy, which we discussed at length in Part II. Compassionate caregivers are at some risk of getting overwhelmed by the suffering of the one who is dying. For example, the diagnosis of a life-threatening illness such as cancer often renders a person numb and stunned. A loved one sitting with them as the diagnosis is communicated will likely experience similar feelings, and yet it is important for them to be able to function so as to help the other cope.

Patients experience the compassion of their professional and family caregivers through simple gestures such as a hug, a gentle touch on the shoulder, or "kind eyes." To look on another's suffering with kind eyes is to take that suffering in to one's heart and hold it there gently. For the family caregiver experiencing their own pain as well, this can be very difficult, perhaps impossible, initially. Their distress, as well as that of their loved one, calls for comfort, posing an even more formidable challenge for the medical team. The team itself may become numbed to the suffering of patients, indeed may need to be shielded from the sheer volume of distress pumped into their world each day, as a dozen or more patients receive the news that their cancer has spread. Imagine the challenge of being compassionate to 20 or 30 patients and family members facing life-threatening circumstances each day. Compassionate caregivers must themselves find sources to nourish their care. Paradoxically, one source of compassion can be the very patients and families who need their care.

Humor is a saving grace in mortal time, as in all of life. People facing frightening circumstances cannot sustain the energy necessary to stay frightened over long periods. They need relief from tension. Humor can be profoundly healing in times of intense distress, but must be used tactfully since it can backfire and send a message of disrespect. Knowing a person's sensibilities is important here, because what evokes laughter in one person might cause acute pain for another. This is a place where it is important to follow the lead of the other. Sometimes a person's sense of humor in these circumstances can be striking. People cry and laugh even in the midst of horrendous suffering, fear, and distress. There can be healthy forms of expressing humor as well as maladaptive ones, where humor appears to be masking deep sorrow, in the effort to stave off grieving that might be necessary for acceptance.

A patient illustrated his own appreciation for irony and good sense of humor when he reflected, "It's amazing how nice people are to you when they think you're going to die." He had recently undergone a life-threatening treatment and returned home safely. His comment was recalling how friends and relatives treated him after his initial diagnosis, when it was felt that there was little that medical treatment could offer him and before he traveled across country to Seattle for a life-saving and risky bone marrow transplant. This is an excellent example of the saving grace of a sense of humor. He was able to laugh at his own peculiar circumstances, at how he saw others seeing him.

Healing can occur when humor and laughter enter mortal-time conversation, sometimes in very unusual ways. So called "gallows humor" can lighten the burden of both patient and caregiver. One patient joked, "I won't have to worry about paying my life insurance premiums any more!" This type of humor has risks and is best initiated by the patient rather than the caregiver. An example of a statement that could be hurtful is the following, overheard in a busy cancer clinic: "Are you still alive?" A professional caregiver asked that question to a patient that he had not seen in a long time. The patient and professional both laughed heartily and began a brief conversation. This appeared to go over well because the question was posed in a joking manner. However, one can see how this might be upsetting to a patient, and linger on in their imagination in the form of questions, such as, "I wonder what he meant by that; does he expect me to die soon?" Humor, like fire, can warm or burn.

Finally, the caregiver who is a family member of a loved one or a professional working with patients daily must come to some *awareness of their own limitations*. The caregiver cannot take all the pain away when life-threatening illness arrives. One who loves or cares for another will suffer when they do. We cannot spare our loved ones the sorrow and pain that is a part of each and every one of our lives. This may be the hardest reality of the hard lessons in being a faithful companion in mortal time—we are limited in our ability to protect those we love from suffering.

Every companion has physical and emotional limitations that will be reached. For example, knowing when the limits of physical endurance have been reached will help caregivers avoid complete exhaustion. We have seen professional and family companions push the limits of endurance and make themselves sick. A wise companion learns when to stop and take a break.

Consideration and Spontaneity

Most people are not comfortable talking with friends and relatives about life-threatening illness or the possibility of dying, and often turn to professionals or self-help books for advice. The father's statement that we quoted—"I don't know what to say. I don't know what I should say. And, he doesn't know what to say to me."—illustrates the initial awkwardness that most people experience in the mortal time zone. Most people can discover the words, if they can find the heart, for conversation in mortal time. As noted earlier, the basic ground rules for respectful communication do not change in mortal time even though the topic of dying may be much more difficult to face. In the everyday give-and-take of conversation, spontaneity is one life-giving element, a source of much joy for human beings. However, spontaneous comments without some disciplined consideration of the psychological and spiritual state of those facing the possibility of death can cause unintended pain. For example, it is not uncommon for a well-meaning friend or relative to respond thoughtlessly to a person facing life-threatening illness. The listener tries to reach out, but does so in a painful, spontaneous, and harmful way.

Spontaneity Without Consideration

Sheila's new diagnosis of breast cancer had come as a shock to her. However, after her initial surgical treatment she was adjusting reasonably well even with the prospect of chemotherapy. She recounted that she had been describing her treatment and how she was doing to a friend. The friend proceeded to blurt out: "Well my aunt had breast cancer and chemotherapy too. The chemotherapy was unbelievably difficult. It almost killed her. She did live several years after that and then her cancer came back. It always comes back."

Sheila was stunned and frightened by her friend's comments, an example of a spontaneous and thoughtless statement. A volunteer in our cancer center tells of overhearing the following comment spoken by a caregiver of one patient to another patient in the waiting area: "Oh, my mother had that and she was gone in three weeks." It is not difficult to imagine how such words might affect a patient just beginning chemotherapy.

Spontaneous Humor Can Backfire

With some embarrassment and obvious remorse, a very thoughtful and spontaneous practitioner tells the following story. One of his patients had undergone more than one course of radiation therapy. Unfortunately her tumors returned on several occasions. During an office visit, her physician, in a moment of spontaneous and light exchange commented, "You are just a little tumor-making machine aren't you?" Several months later when the patient screwed up her courage and told him how that comment had hurt and scared her, he was embarrassed and self-critical. He had intended the comment to be humorous and upon reflection was surprised at his own "foot-in-mouth" question to her, saying, "How could I have said that?" We all have tactless moments; however, not all caregivers are as mature and open as this practitioner, who had built a relationship of trust that eventually led to another conversation where the comment was discussed, the patient could express her feelings, and he could offer his apology.

Censored Conversation vs. Active Listening

On the other end of the continuum of spontaneous interchange is the person who censors all responses containing potentially disturbing information. This results in hesitant, polite, and distant comments devoid of life-giving energy like, "I am sure everything will work out all right." Compassionate conversation requires spontaneity, consideration, and disciplined understanding of the person's situation. This skill demands active, careful listening first before responding with words. Of course the act of being present and attentive is a very powerful and healing response in and of itself. We must listen with compassion and speak the truth in love.

The best intentions to remain calm and open in the presence of a suffering loved one can dissolve in tears or give way to mute anxiety when the caregiver is confronted with the stark possibility of a loved one dying. When someone we care about says, "There is no cure now, the cancer is moving. Is there any hope?" Any caregiver will be challenged to find a spontaneous yet disciplined and helpful response. Professional caregivers may learn how to be disciplined with so many opportunities. Their challenge will be to remain spontaneous. Family caregivers may be spontaneous yet with little experience, undisciplined in the nuances of healing conversation. In our closing section we address the following question often asked of caregivers, both family and professional: How do you do this anyway?

Part III: For Those Who Have Never Died —Questions for Reflection and Conversation

The following questions are provided to help you reflect on the ideas presented in the text. They can be used to deepen your understanding of how these concepts apply to you. Or you can use them to stimulate discussion between you and another person or members of a group.

1. Have you ever been a companion for someone who has entered mortal time, someone with a life-threatening illness? How did this affect you?

2. Have you had a kind companion walk with you in difficult times? How was that helpful?

3. What are some of the risks to companioning someone in mortal time?

4. How have you cultivated the qualities necessary for taking part in healing conversation? Where have you experienced sensitivity, courage, acceptance, respect, compassion, presence, and humor in your life?

5. What does it mean to be sensitive to another person's feelings? How might the virtue of sensitivity be valuable in mortal time?

6. How capable are you of accepting mortal time? Can you "let go" when the time is right?

7. How might you cultivate compassion in yourself? What does it mean for you to practice compassion?

8. What are some of the obstacles to maintaining presence with those in mortal time? How do you overcome them?

9. How do you use humor to help manage different conversations? Have you seen attempts at humor backfire? How? What happened?

10. Can you "let go" when the time is right? How do you do it?

CLOSING
A WORD TO CAREGIVERS

"How can you do this anyway?" This question is often asked of professional caregivers by patients, family members, and those unfamiliar with the challenge and promise of mortal time. It is also a question for anybody who is a caregiver of a seriously ill family member, a likely role for all of us at one time or another. One answer is that meeting others with compassion and honesty in mortal time has many intrinsic rewards, including a deep satisfaction at helping others, which increases our own capacity to love. Caring for another may in fact be a gift to oneself, a pouring out of one's own cup of caring that can fill it back up. Giving becomes receiving.

Resilience and Absorbing Suffering

As we have said, once-in-a-lifetime, shattering events for patients and their families and friends are "normal" for a professional caregiver. How can a person be repeatedly exposed to the shocking entrance into mortal time without becoming depressed or unglued? Traveling regularly on the ground of mortal time requires and develops two personal qualities. The first is psychological resilience, which is the capacity to adapt well in the face of adversity. A serious life-threatening illness will tax anyone and being resilient does not mean that no emotional distress will be experienced. On the contrary, emotional pain and suffering are inevitable, even for the resilient person. Resilience is not a quality that people either have or not. We all have some and what we have can be deepened intentionally. However, some people seem to develop this capacity more deeply than others. One quality of resilient people is the capacity to manage strong feelings and impulses. We know a physician who has a custom of taking a deep breath and offering a short prayer before entering the exam room of her next cancer patient, thereby restoring herself from her previous encounter and preparing herself for her next. This is just one example of a simple, practical way to remain effective and resilient in a hectic clinic full of patients and caregivers managing their lives in mortal time.

The second quality necessary for traveling in mortal time is the capacity to absorb suffering without becoming overwhelmed by it. Some have referred to this as establishing psychological boundaries, so that at the end of the day the professional caregiver can go home and, for the most part, leave the suffering behind. But what professional caregiver doesn't periodically lie awake at night, troubled by their patient's struggle? Of course, the family caregiver, particularly the primary caregiver, is more exposed, for they will not be able to leave their situation behind as professional caregivers do every day.

One cannot enter conversation about mortal time with an open heart and remain untouched. It hurts to encounter the suffering of another. However, healing and helping in the midst of suffering is an altruistic act and can be its own reward. We can become "larger" when we listen and empathize with the life story of another. Bernard Loomer describes this phenomenon figuratively as "growing in stature": our soul expands in size. [1] This happens whenever we compassionately take in the life experience of another person, in this case the suffering of a person struggling in mortal time.

Empathy Shift

What is the downside to daily exposure to the rigors of mortal time? Can day after day in the company of suffering affect a caregiver's emotional sensibility? Yes. Seeing and being with people subjected to suffering has a profound impact on caregiver perception. Some may experience a change in their ability to empathize with the normal and expected small wounds of everyday life. After being confronted with the stark pain and disruption of cancer, how is one to respond to a 15-year-old whose shoes don't quite match the color of her prom dress? Or the cold and flu-like symptoms of a spouse? As a colleague so aptly puts it, "It takes a lot more to get my attention—If it isn't cancer, just get over it." If, as we suggested in Part II, empathy is the capacity to "walk in another's shoes," chronic exposure to severe health problems may limit the caregiver's ability to empathize with a person experiencing everyday non-life-threatening health problems. The caregiver's empathy threshold shifts such that distress experienced by someone has to be a lot greater in order to reach the point where it triggers an empathic response. Another's suffering may need to be acute to activate the ability of the professional caregiver to respond empathically. The phenomenon of diminished empathy, or empathy shift, can have major implications for the day-to-day communication of caregivers with those outside the kingdom of suffering.

Sharing the Darkness

Conversation in mortal time exposes both the caregiver and the person who may be dying to powerful psychological forces. Two metaphors can illuminate these forces. The first, described by physician Sheila Cassidy, concerns darkness. Dr. Cassidy calls the experience of suffering with another "sharing the darkness." [2] The caregiver proceeding into mortal time with another does so at personal risk, for in sharing the darkness, one cannot help but absorb some of it into one's soul. In a real conversation with one who is awake in mortal time, the most healthy and psychologically resilient caregiver will experience this darkening as he or she loses the comforting but false presumption of time's endlessness. Encountering death is not for the faint of heart, but, paradoxically, strength does not lie in stoic, unemotional encounter but rather in awareness and acceptance of one's own emotional responses, including intense anxiety. In the deepening shade of mortal time, caregivers can begin to see more clearly their own lives as they encounter vicariously the prospect of their own deaths.

Invisible Mending

The second metaphor comes from the C.K. Williams poem entitled "Invisible Mending." [3] In the poem, Williams depicts three old women, sewing and using "their amputating shears: forgiveness and repair." He compares sewing garments with the tasks of forgiveness and repair that necessarily accompany all human relating. The emotional healing that occurs in conversation in mortal time is a form of invisible mending. This image is also captured in the Jewish conception of the human vocation—*tikkun olam*—to bind up the world's brokenness.

The transformative possibility embedded in the experience of mortal time derives from facing death as the potential limit of all human existence. This disturbing possibility in turn carries the blessed opportunity to consider one's life, make amends where possible, and say what is in one's heart to family, friends, and associates—to finish one's life with deliberateness and a measure of closure denied to those who die suddenly or who "successfully" evade the awareness of mortality.

The claim we make in these pages is simple, but never easy to honor: Whatever the details of a life-threatening illness, and however great the differences in backgrounds, roles, and responsibilities of those communicating about it, authentic conversation has the power to enhance how people cope with living in mortal time. Real talking and listening can illuminate and enrich the very meaning of life for patients and caregivers alike as they inhabit this sacred place together. The liberating possibility embedded in the experience of mortal time is the freedom that can come from facing death squarely as the limit of our existence. We must embrace what we mortals fear and ordinarily avoid with every fiber of our being. We must turn toward death together.

Closing—Questions for Reflection and Conversation

The following questions are provided to help you reflect on the ideas presented in the text. They can be used to deepen your understanding of how these concepts apply to you. Or you can use them to stimulate discussion between you and another person or members of a group.

1. Have you been tested with a major life-threatening illness? How would you rate your own psychological resilience? Can you usually adapt to life stressors quickly or do you need time to adjust?

2. How do you rate your own ability to absorb suffering and still function each day? Have you been subjected to periods of suffering yourself or with a loved one or patient? Describe how you managed during that time?

3. Have you experienced "empathy shift" in your personal or professional life? What was this like for you?

4. Do you have someone that you have "shared the darkness with?" What was that like for you?

5. Have you experienced the "invisible mending" of conversation? Describe the situation and the circumstances under which this occurred? How did you feel about it?

6. How can awareness of our own position in mortal time be both alarming and liberating?

NOTES

Prologue

1. "On Earth," from *Walking to Martha's Vineyard* (New York: Knopf, 2003), 4, by Franz Wright, copyright © by Franz Wright. Used by permission of Alfred A. Knopf, a division of Random House, Inc.

Opening

1. Parts of this book have appeared in two previously published articles: M.A. Cowan and R.P. McQuellon, "Turning toward death together," *The Furrow* (July/August 2000): 395-402; and R.P. McQuellon and M.A. Cowan, "Turning toward death together: Conversation in mortal time," *The American Journal of Hospice & Palliative Care* 17 (2000): 9, 312-318.

2. M. Lerner, *Choices in Healing: Integrating the Best of Conventional and Complementary Approaches to Cancer* (Cambridge, MA: MIT Press, 1996), xix.

Part I: The Many Meanings of Mortal Time

1. The lines reproduced here are from Theodore Roethke's poem "In a Dark Time," which appears in *The Collected Poems of Theodore Roethke* (New York: Doubleday, 1966), 231.

2. We are indebted to Barbara Sourkes and her explication of the concept "neutral time." See B. Sourkes, *The Deepening Shade: Psychological Aspects of Life-Threatening Illness* (Pittsburg: University of Pittsburg Press, 1982). Dr. Sourkes acknowledges Margaret Clare Kiely who coined the term "neutral time" to capture the experience of patients who enter this "living-dying interval."

3. J.D. Frank and J.B. Frank, *Persuasion and Healing: A Comparative Study of Psychotherapy* (Rev. Ed.) (Baltimore: Johns Hopkins University Press, 1973).

4. R. Janoff-Bulman, *Shattered Assumptions: Toward a Psychology of Trauma* (New York: Free Press, 1992).

5. D.F. Cella, "Health promotion in oncology: A cancer wellness doctrine," *Journal of Psychosocial Oncology* 8 (1990): 1, 17-31.

6. C.M. Orsborn et al., *Speak the Language of Healing: Living with Breast Cancer Without Going to War* (Berkeley: Conari Press, 1989).

7. A. Ornstein, "The dread to repeat," *Journal of the American Psychoanalytic Association* 39 (1989): 377-398.

8. C. Geertz, *The Interpretation of Cultures* (New York: Basic Books, 1973), 100-108.

9. M. Heidegger, *Being and Time,* trans. J. Stambaugh (Albany: SUNY Press, 1996).

10. Cited in E.T. Chambers and M.A. Cowan, *Roots for Radicals* (New York: Continuum, 2005), 59.

11. H. Sigler, *Hollis Sigler's Breast Cancer Journal* (New York: Hudson Hills Press, 1999).

12. J. Kabat-Zinn, *Wherever You Go, There You Are: Mindfulness Meditation in Everyday Life* (New York: Hyperion Books, 1994).

13. Personal communication with Richard McQuellon, January 15, 1993. Also, see Bob Stone and Jenny Stone Humphries, *Where the Buffaloes Roam: Building a Team for Life's Challenges* (Boston: Addison Wesley Publishing Company, 1993).

14. R.G. Smith, *Martin Buber* (Richmond: John Knox Press, 1967), 14.

Part II: Hope from Conversation

1. G. Marcel, *Tragic Wisdom and Beyond* (Evanston: Northwestern University Press, 1973), 143.

2. V. Havel, *Disturbing the Peace: A Conversation with Karel Huizdala* (New York: Random House, 1991), 199.

3. Stephen Jay Gould, "The Median Isn't the Message," *Steve Dunn's CancerGuide*, http://cancerguide.org/median_not_msg.html (26 August 2007).

4. A. Broyard, *Intoxicated by My Illness: And Other Writings on Life and Death* (New York: Crown Publishers: 1992).

5. L.A. Fogarty, B.A. Curbow, J.R. Wingard, K. McDonnell, and M.R. Somerfield, "Can 40 seconds of compassion reduce patient anxiety?" *Journal of Clinical Oncology* 17 (1999): 1, 371-379.

6. Ephesians 4: 15, *The New Oxford Annotated Bible* (New York: Oxford University Press. 1991).

7. William Shakespeare, *Julius Caesar* 2.2.32-34, in *The Complete Works of William Shakespeare* (Roslyn, NY: Walter J. Black, 1937), 870.

8. J. Rieveschl and M. Cowan, *Selfhood and the Dance of Empathy. Progress in Self Psychology*, vol. 19 (Hillsdale, NJ: The Analytic Press, 2003), 107-132.

9. Nina Ann Stokes was a courageous volunteer, colleague, and breast cancer patient who managed her diagnosis and many recurrences and treatments with grace and determination. She was an inspiration to members of the Cancer Patient Support Program community. She died on March 14, 2001, nine years after her initial diagnosis. After one of her many treatments she developed peripheral neuropathy. Peripheral neuropathy is a condition caused by damage to the nerves in the peripheral nervous system. Many of these nerves are involved with sensation and feeling things such as pain, temperature, and touch. Peripheral neuropathy is usually felt at first as tingling and numbness in the

hands and feet. Symptoms can be described as burning, shooting pain, throbbing, aching, and "feels like frostbite" or "walking on a bed of coals." It is most commonly a side effect of some drugs used to treat cancer.

10. W.I. Thomas and D.S. Thomas, *The Child in America* (NY: Knopf, 1928), 572.

11. E. Fox, K. Landrum-McNiff, Z. Zhong, N.V. Dawson, A.W. Wu, and J. Lynn, "Evaluation of prognostic criteria for determining hospice eligibility in patients with advanced lung, heart, or liver cancer," *JAMA* 282 (1999): 1638-1645. This study points out that some chronically ill patients may "never experience a time during which they are clearly dying of their disease." By "clearly dying" the authors are referring to acute symptoms that are imminently life threatening. Predicting the length of remaining life probably is best done on the following continuum: hours to days, days to weeks, weeks to months, and months to years. Indeed some hospice patients graduate to home rather than the grave yard.

12. Anton Chekhov, "Misery—To Whom Shall I Tell My Grief?" in *Anton Chekhov's Short Stories*, ed. Ralph E. Maitlaw (New York: W.W. Norton & Co., 1979), 11-16.

13. C.L. Loprinzi, M.E. Johnson, and G. Steer, "Doc, how much time do I have?" *Journal of Clinical Oncology* 18 (2000) 3, 699-701.

14. D.G. Larson and D.R. Tobin, "End of life conversations: evolving practice and theory," *JAMA* 284 (2000):12, 1573-1578.

Part III: For Those Who Have Never Died

1. Ecclesiastes 3:1, *The New Oxford Annotated Bible* (New York: Oxford University Press. 1991).

2. L.G. Calhoun and R.G. Tedeschi, "Expert companions: Posttraumatic growth in clinical practice," in *Handbook of Post-*

traumatic Growth, eds. Calhoun and Tedeschi (Mahwah, NJ: Lawrence Erlbaum Associates, Inc., 2006).

3. We are grateful to Dr. Richard Tedeschi for his thoughtful explanation of the qualities necessary for expert companioning in a lecture he gave at the Wake Forest University Baptist Medical Center Comprehensive Cancer Center, September 1, 2006.

Closing: A Word to Caregivers

1. B. Loomer, "S-I-Z-E is the measure," in *Religious Experience and Process Theology*, eds. H. Cargas and B. Lee (NY: Paulist Press, 1976) 69-76.

2. S. Cassidy, *Sharing the Darkness: the Spirituality of Caring* (Marynoll, NY: Orbis Books, 1991). In her fine work, Dr. Cassidy quotes Anglican author J. B. Phillips. Suffering from deep depression, Phillips "shared this darkness" with a colleague, noting, "There is no way out, only a way forward."

3. C.K. Williams, *Repair* (New York: Farrar, Straus and Giroux, 1999).

BIBLIOGRAPHY

Broyard, A. *Intoxicated by My Illness: And Other Writings on Life and Death.* New York: Crown Publishers: 1992.

Calhoun, L.G., and R.G. Tedeschi. "Expert companions: Posttraumatic growth in clinical practice." In *Handbook of Posttraumatic Growth.* Edited by Calhoun and Tedeschi. Mahwah, NJ: Lawrence Erlbaum Associates, Inc., 2006.

Cassidy, S. *Sharing the Darkness: the Spirituality of Caring.* Marynoll, NY: Orbis Books, 1991.

Cella, D.F. "Health promotion in oncology: A cancer wellness doctrine." *Journal of Psychosocial Oncology* 8 (1990): 1, 17-31.

Chambers, E.T., and M.A. Cowan, *Roots for Radicals.* New York: Continuum, 2005.

Chekhov, A. "Misery—To Whom Shall I Tell My Grief?" In *Anton Chekhov's Short Stories.* Edited by Ralph E. Maitlaw, 11-16. New York: W.W. Norton & Co., 1979.

Cowan, M.A., and R.P. McQuellon. "Turning toward death together." *The Furrow* (July/August 2000): 395-402.

Fogarty, L.A., B.A. Curbow, J.R. Wingard, K. McDonnell, and M.R. Somerfield. "Can 40 seconds of compassion reduce patient anxiety?" *Journal of Clinical Oncology* 17 (1999): 1, 371-379.

Fox, E., K. Landrum-McNiff, Z. Zhong, N.V. Dawson, A.W. Wu, and J. Lynn. "Evaluation of prognostic criteria for determining hospice eligibility in patients with advanced lung, heart, or liver cancer." *JAMA* 282 (1999): 1638-1645.

Frank, J.D., and J.B. Frank. *Persuasion and Healing: A Comparative Study of Psychotherapy.* (Rev. Ed.) Baltimore: Johns Hopkins University Press, 1973.

Geertz, C. *The Interpretation of Cultures.* New York: Basic Books, 1973.

Gould, S.J. "The Median Isn't the Message." *Steve Dunn's Cancer Guide*. http://cancerguide.org/median_not_msg.html.

Havel, V. *Disturbing the Peace: A Conversation with Karel Huizdala*. New York: Random House, 1991.

Heidegger, M. *Being and Time*. Translated by J. Stambaugh. Albany: SUNY Press, 1996.

Janoff-Bulman, R. *Shattered Assumptions: Toward a Psychology of Trauma*. New York: Free Press, 1992.

Kabat-Zinn, J. *Wherever You Go, There You Are: Mindfulness Meditation in Everyday Life*. New York: Hyperion Books, 1994.

Larson, D.G., and D.R. Tobin. "End of life conversations: evolving practice and theory." *JAMA* 284 (2000):12, 1573-1578.

Lerner M. *Choices in Healing: Integrating the Best of Conventional and Complementary Approaches to Cancer*. Cambridge, MA: MIT Press, 1996.

Loomer, B. "S-I-Z-E is the measure." In *Religious Experience and Process Theology*. Edited by H. Cargas and B. Lee, 69-76. NY: Paulist Press, 1976.

Loprinzi, C.L., M.E. Johnson, and G. Steer. "Doc, how much time do I have?" *Journal of Clinical Oncology* 18 (2000) 3, 699-701.

Marcel, G. *Tragic Wisdom and Beyond*. Evanston: Northwestern University Press, 1973.

McQuellon, R.P., and M.A. Cowan. "Turning toward death together: Conversation in mortal time." *The American Journal of Hospice & Palliative Care* 17 (2000): 9, 312-318.

The New Oxford Annotated Bible. New York: Oxford University Press. 1991.

Ornstein A. "The dread to repeat." *Journal of the American Psychoanalytic Association* 39 (1989): 377-398.

Orsborn, C.M., L. Quigley, K.L. Stroup, and S. Kuner. *Speak the Language of Healing: Living with Breast Cancer Without Going to War*. Berkeley: Conari Press, 1989.

Rieveschl, J., and M. Cowan. *Selfhood and the Dance of Empathy. Progress in Self Psychology.* Vol. 19. Hillsdale, NJ: The Analytic Press, 2003.

Roethke, T. "In a Dark Time." In *The Collected Poems of Theodore Roethke*, 231. New York: Doubleday, 1966.

Shakespeare, W. *Julius Caesar.* In *The Complete Works of William Shakespeare*, 860-888. Roslyn, NY: Walter J. Black, 1937.

Sigler, H. *Hollis Sigler's Breast Cancer Journal.* New York: Hudson Hills Press, 1999.

Smith, R.G. *Martin Buber.* Richmond: John Knox Press, 1967.

Sourkes, B. *The Deepening Shade: Psychological Aspects of Life-Threatening Illness.* Pittsburg: University of Pittsburg Press, 1982.

Stone, B., and J.S. Humphries. *Where the Buffaloes Roam: Building a Team for Life's Challenges.* Boston: Addison Wesley Publishing Company, 1993.

Thomas, W.I., and D.S. Thomas. *The Child in America.* NY: Knopf, 1928.

Williams, C.K. *Repair.* New York: Farrar, Straus and Giroux, 1999.

Wright, F. "On Earth." In *Walking to Martha's Vineyard, 4.* New York: Knopf, 2003.